CONTENTS

ISBN 0-8497-6277-4

Unit 1
Meter

Meter is the grouping of beats into units of equal size called measures. The meter of a composition is indicated by the time signature.

Duple, Triple, and Quadruple Meter

Music with *two* beats in each measure is called **duple meter.**

Music with *three* beats in each measure is called **triple meter.**

Music with *four* beats in each measure is called **quadruple meter.**

Simple and Compound Meter

In **simple meter,** the beat can be divided by two:
The top number in the time signature will be 2, 3, or 4.

Simple Duple Meter:

Simple Triple Meter:

Simple Quadruple Meter:

In **compound meter,** the beat can be divided by three:
The top number in the time signature will be 6, 9, or 12.

Compound Duple Meter:

Compound Triple Meter:

Compound Quadruple Meter:

Irregular Meter

When the top number in the time signature is 5 or 7, it is called **irregular meter.**

From *Sonata No. 7* by Prokofiev
From *Sonatine* by Ravel

Changing Meter

When the time signature changes within a piece of music, it is called **changing meter.**

From *Evening in the Country* by Bartok

1. Name each meter. Add bar lines to divide each rhythm into measures. Write in the counts.

Unit 2
Key Signatures

The Circle of Keys

The **circle of keys** is a diagram of all Major and minor key signatures. The sharp keys are arranged from the top, moving clockwise. The flat keys are arranged from the top, moving counter clockwise.

There are fifteen Major keys: seven sharp keys, seven flat keys, and one key with no sharps or flats. Likewise, there are fifteen relative minor keys.

The keys at the bottom of the circle are called **enharmonic** keys because their tones sound the same but are named and written differently.

The circle of keys is sometimes called the **circle of fifths** because the keys are arranged an interval of a fifth apart. Notice that as you move around the circle clockwise from the top, one new sharp is added to each key. As you move around the circle counter clockwise from the top, one new flat is added to each key.

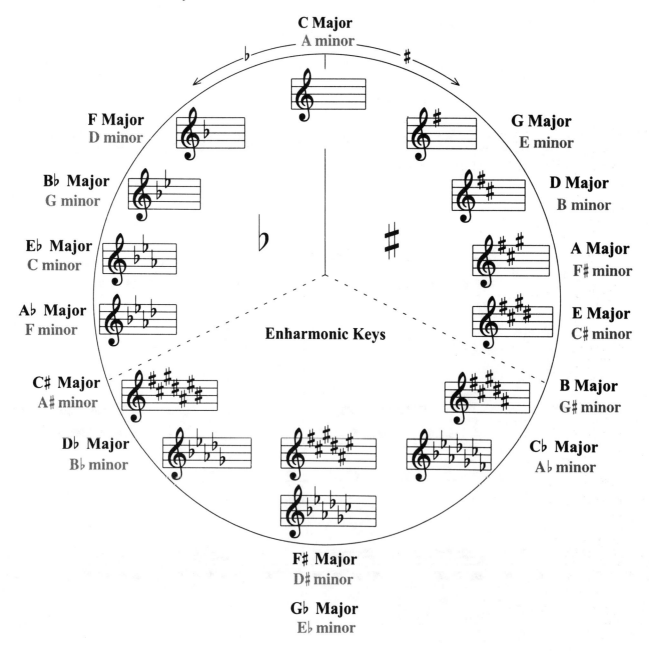

1. Write the Major and minor name for each key signature.

| _____ Major | _____ Major | _____ Major | _____ Major | _____ Major |
| _____ minor | _____ minor | _____ minor | _____ minor | _____ minor |

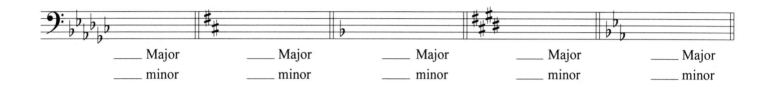

| _____ Major | _____ Major | _____ Major | _____ Major | _____ Major |
| _____ minor | _____ minor | _____ minor | _____ minor | _____ minor |

| _____ Major | _____ Major | _____ Major | _____ Major | _____ Major |
| _____ minor | _____ minor | _____ minor | _____ minor | _____ minor |

2. Write each key signature.

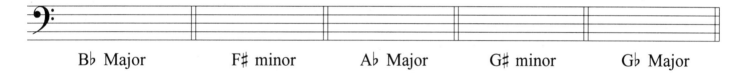

| B♭ Major | F♯ minor | A♭ Major | G♯ minor | G♭ Major |

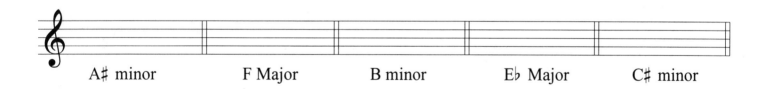

| A♯ minor | F Major | B minor | E♭ Major | C♯ minor |

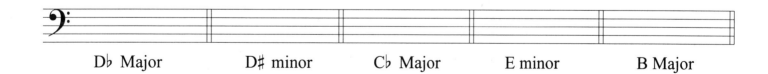

| D♭ Major | D♯ minor | C♭ Major | E minor | B Major |

Unit 3
Scales

Major Scales

All **Major scales** are formed with the same pattern of half steps and whole steps:
whole - whole - **half** - whole - whole - whole - **half**

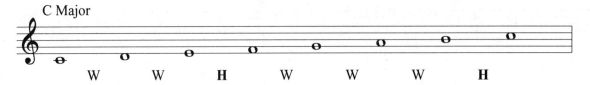

1. Add the correct sharps or flats to form each Major scale (do not use a key signature).
   Check your answers by referring to the Circle of Keys on page 4.

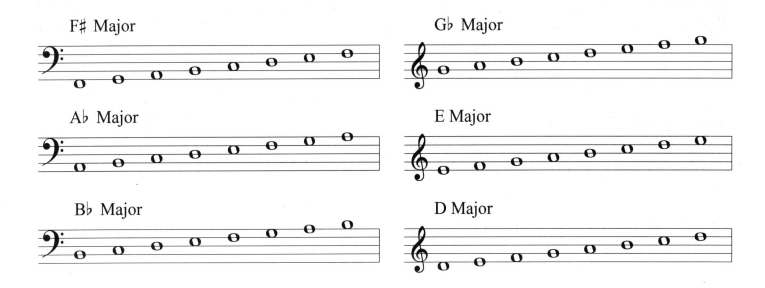

2. Draw the notes of each Major scale ascending. Use whole notes. Add the correct sharps or flats to form each scale (do not use a key signature). Check your answers by referring to the Circle of Keys on page 4.

Relative Minor Scales

Each Major scale has a relative minor scale with the same key signature.
The sixth note of the Major scale is the first note of the minor scale.

3. Draw the notes of each Major and relative minor scale indicated by the key signature.

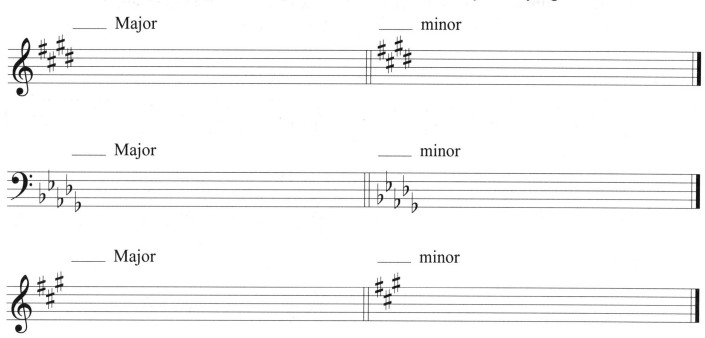

_____ Major   _____ minor

_____ Major   _____ minor

_____ Major   _____ minor

4. Write the key signature indicated, then draw the notes of the minor scale.

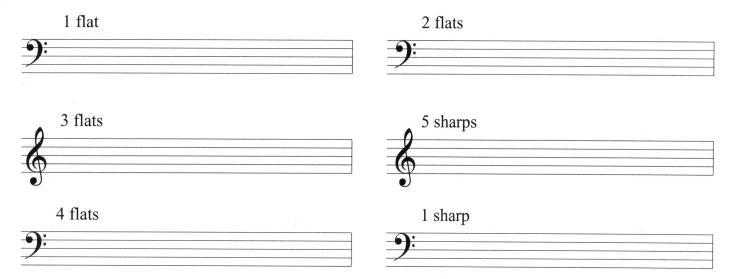

1 flat   2 flats

3 flats   5 sharps

4 flats   1 sharp

Forms of Minor Scales

There are three forms of minor scales: **natural, harmonic** and **melodic.** The **natural** minor scale follows the key signature exactly: none of the notes are changed. The **harmonic** minor scale has a raised 7th note (1/2 step). The **melodic** minor scale has a raised 6th and 7th note ascending, and then lowered descending. The melodic minor scale descending uses the same notes as the natural minor scale. The altered notes in the harmonic and melodic minor scales must be written in as accidentals because the key signature does not change.

5. Change these natural minor scales to **harmonic** minor scales by adding the correct accidentals.

6. Change these natural minor scales to **melodic** minor scales by adding the correct accidentals.

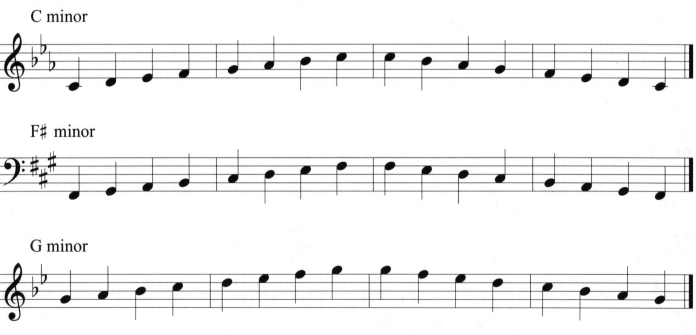

Parallel Major and Minor Scales

Parallel Major and minor scales have the same tonic note. A shift between parallel Major and minor can occur with a change of key signature or with the use of accidentals.

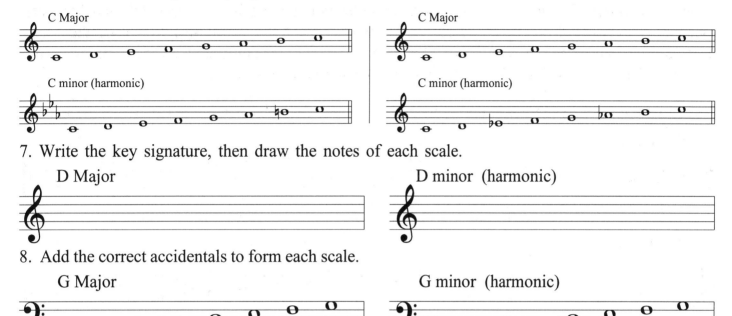

7. Write the key signature, then draw the notes of each scale.

D Major   D minor (harmonic)

8. Add the correct accidentals to form each scale.

G Major   G minor (harmonic)

Whole Tone Scale

A **whole tone scale** is made entirely of whole steps. There are only two sets of tones upon which a whole tone scale may be formed. Each set has six tones.

Set 1   Set 2

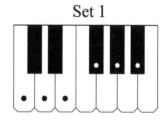   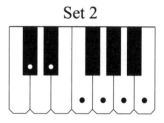

A whole tone scale can begin on any note. The notes can be written with a variety of enharmonic spellings, for example:

or

9. Draw six notes to complete each whole tone scale.

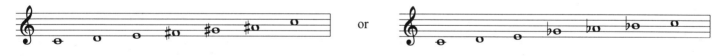

10. Rewrite this whole tone scale with enharmonic spellings for the notes that are sharp.

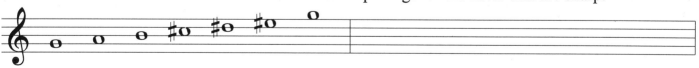

Unit 4
Intervals

The distance between two notes is called an **interval.**

Interval Qualities

- 2nds, 3rds, 6ths and 7ths may be Major, minor, diminished or Augmented.
- 4ths, 5ths and 8ths (octaves) may be Perfect, diminished or Augmented.

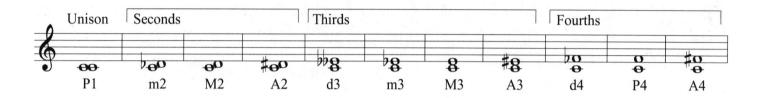

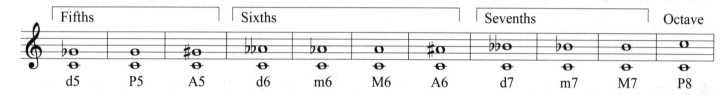

Harmonic and Melodic Intervals

Two notes played together form a **harmonic** interval. Two notes played one at a time form a **melodic** interval.

1. Identify each interval. Write **M** for Major, **m** for minor, **P** for Perfect, **d** for diminished and **A** for Augmented.

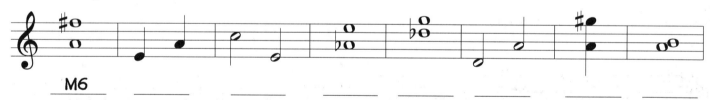

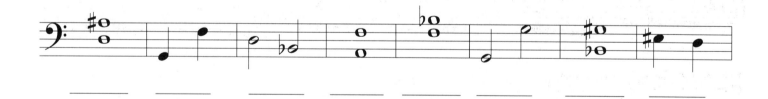

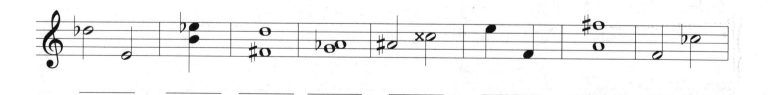

2. Draw one note above the given one to form each interval.

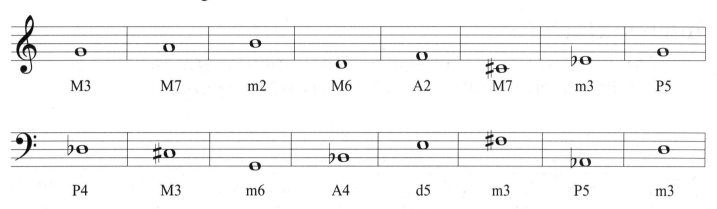

M3   M7   m2   M6   A2   M7   m3   P5

P4   M3   m6   A4   d5   m3   P5   m3

3. Write the name of each interval on the lines above and below these music excerpts.

From *Bourree* (French Suite No. 6) by Bach
(*Piano Repertoire: Baroque & Classical,* Level 10)

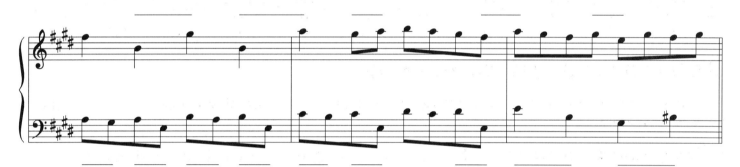

From *Sonata, Hob. XVI:34* by Haydn
(*Piano Repertoire: Baroque & Classical,* Level 10)

From *Rhapsody, Op. 11, No. 3,* by Dohnanyi
(*Piano Repertoire: Romantic & 20th Century,* Level 10)

Unit 5
Triads

A **triad** is a three note chord. The notes of a triad are called the root, 3rd, and 5th. The root names the triad.

G Major Triad

Triad Qualities

Triads may be Major, minor, diminished or Augmented. The **Major** triad has a Perfect 5th and a Major 3rd. The **minor** triad has a Perfect 5th and a minor 3rd. The **diminished** triad has a diminished 5th and minor 3rd. The **Augmented** triad has an Augmented 5th and a Major 3rd.

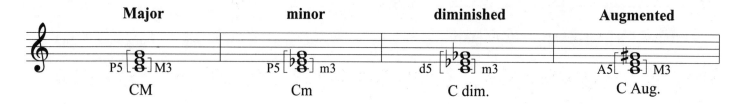

1. Name each triad. Write **M** for Major, **m** for minor, **dim.** for diminished and **Aug.** for Augmented.

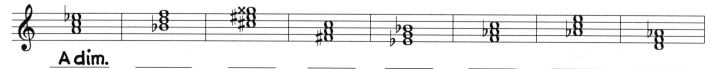

A dim.

2. Write these triads.

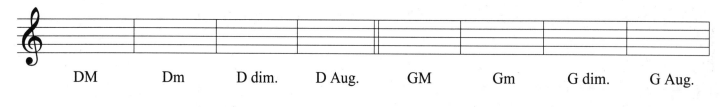

DM   Dm   D dim.   D Aug.   GM   Gm   G dim.   G Aug.

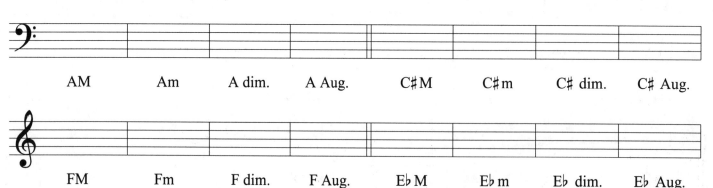

AM   Am   A dim.   A Aug.   C#M   C#m   C# dim.   C# Aug.

FM   Fm   F dim.   F Aug.   Eb M   Eb m   Eb dim.   Eb Aug.

Triads and Inversions

All triads have two **inversions.** A triad is in **root position** when the root of the triad is the lowest note. A triad is in **1st inversion** when the 3rd of the triad is the lowest note. A triad is in **2nd inversion** when the 5th of the triad is the lowest note.

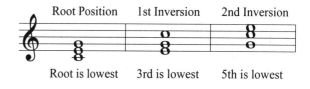

3. Draw the inversions of each root position triad.

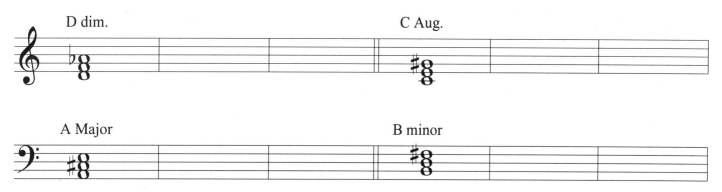

Figured Bass for Triads and Inversions

Figured bass is the use of numbers to identify the inversion of a triad. The figured bass numbers identify the intervals of a triad measured from the bass note (lowest note). The figured bass for a root position triad is $\frac{5}{3}$, however, figured bass is usually omitted for root position triads. The figured bass for a first inversion triad is $\frac{6}{3}$, usually abbreviated to 6. The figured bass for a second inversion triad is $\frac{6}{4}$.

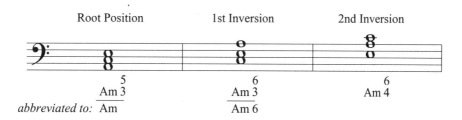

4. Name each triad and write the figured bass.

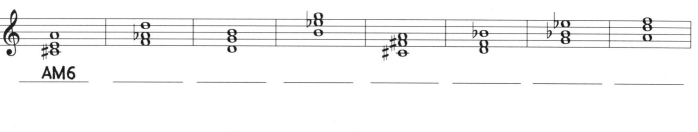

AM6

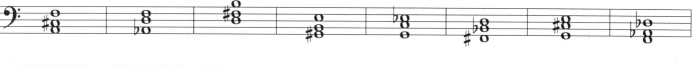

GP670

Triads of Major Scales

A triad may be built on each degree of the Major scale. Each triad is labeled with a Roman numeral.

Major = upper case Roman numeral
minor = lower case Roman numeral
diminished = lower case Roman numeral and °

Each triad is named after the scale degree name of its root.

C Major

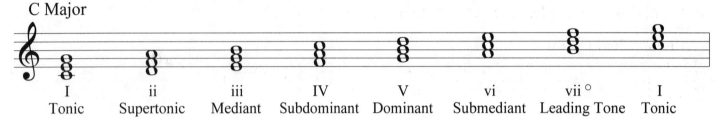

I	ii	iii	IV	V	vi	vii°	I
Tonic	Supertonic	Mediant	Subdominant	Dominant	Submediant	Leading Tone	Tonic

1. Write the Roman numeral and figured bass for each triad of the D♭ Major scale on the lines below the staff. Write the scale degree name for each triad on the lines above the staff.

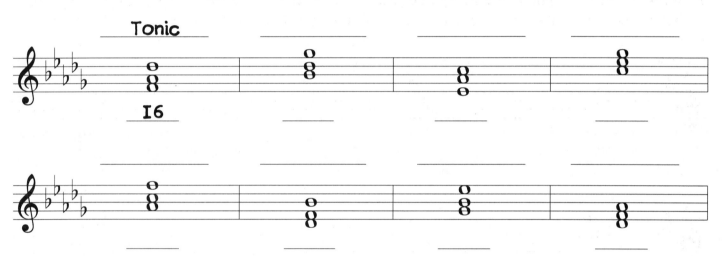

2. Draw each triad of the E Major scale according to the Roman numerals and figured bass. Write the scale degree name for each triad on the lines above the staff.

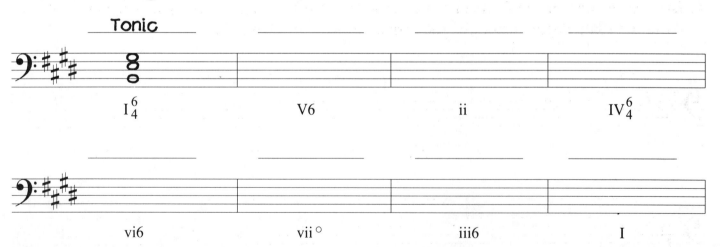

Triads of Minor Scales (Harmonic Form)

A triad may be built on each degree of the minor scale. Each triad is labeled with a Roman numeral.

Major = upper case Roman numeral
minor = lower case Roman numeral
diminished = lower case Roman numeral and °
Augmented = upper case Roman numeral and +

Each triad is named after the scale degree name of its root.

A minor (harmonic)

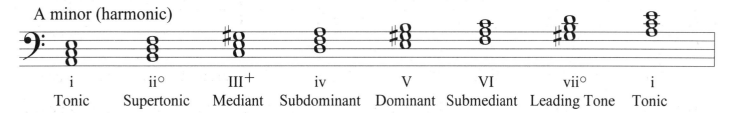

i	ii°	III+	iv	V	VI	vii°	i
Tonic	Supertonic	Mediant	Subdominant	Dominant	Submediant	Leading Tone	Tonic

3. Write the Roman numeral and figured bass for each triad of the B minor scale on the lines below the staff. Write the scale degree name for each triad on the lines above the staff.

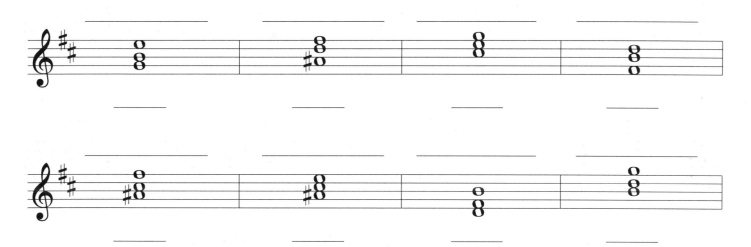

4. Draw each triad of the F minor scale according to the Roman numerals and figured bass. Write the scale degree name for each triad on the lines above the staff.

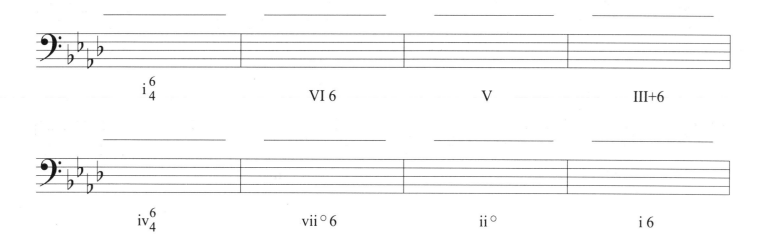

Unit 6
Seventh Chords

A seventh chord is a four note chord. The notes of a seventh chord are called the root, 3rd, 5th, and 7th.

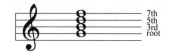

Seventh Chord Qualities

Five qualities of seventh chords are shown below. These seventh chords are formed with the following combinations of triads and 7ths:

- **Major Seventh Chord**: Major triad plus a Major 7th.
- **Dominant Seventh Chord**: Major triad plus a minor 7th.
- **Minor Seventh Chord**: minor triad plus a minor 7th.
- **Half Diminished Seventh Chord**: diminished triad plus a minor 7th.
- **Diminished Seventh Chord**: diminished triad plus a diminished 7th.

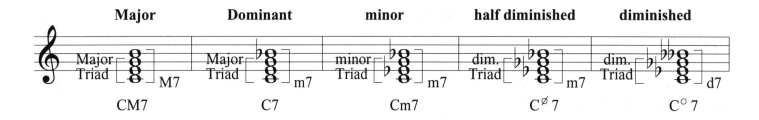

1. Draw Major, Dominant, minor, half diminished and diminished seventh chords on the given roots.

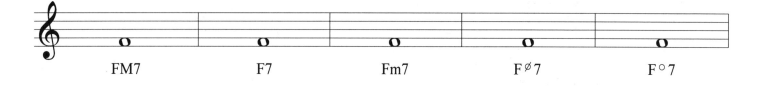

2. Name each seventh chord.

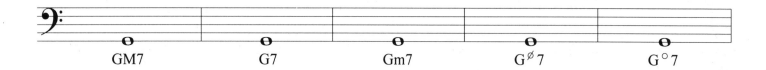

Seventh Chords and Inversions

All seventh chords have three inversions.

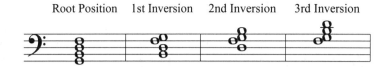

3. Draw the inversions of each root position seventh chord.

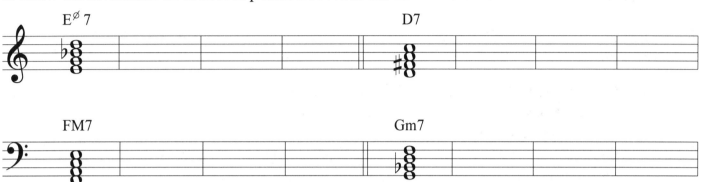

Figured Bass for Seventh Chords and Inversions

Figured bass is used to identify the position of a seventh chord. The figured bass numbers identify the intervals of a seventh chord measured from the bass note (lowest note). The figured bass for a root position seventh chord is $\frac{7}{5}$, abbreviated to 7. The figured bass for a 1st inversion seventh chord is $\frac{6}{5}$, abbreviated to $\frac{6}{5}$. The figured bass for 2nd inversion seventh chords is $\frac{6}{4}$, abbreviated to $\frac{4}{3}$. The figured bass for 3rd inversion seventh chords is $\frac{6}{4}$, abbreviated to $\frac{4}{2}$ or 2.

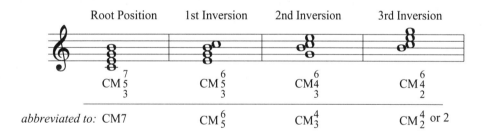

4. Name each seventh chord and write the figured bass.

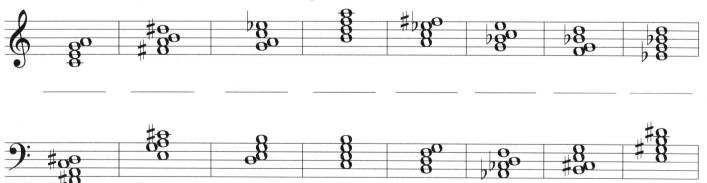

Seventh Chords of Major Scales

A seventh chord may be built on each degree of the Major scale. Each seventh chord is labeled with a Roman numeral and figured bass. Seventh chords built on the tonic and subdominant notes (I and IV) are Major seventh chords. Seventh chords built on the supertonic, mediant and submediant notes (ii, iii and vi) are minor seventh chords. The seventh chord built on the leading tone (vii$^{\o}$) is a half diminished seventh chord. The seventh chord built on the dominant note (V) is the dominant seventh chord.

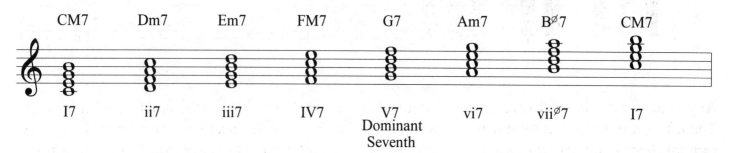

5. Write the Roman numeral and figured bass for each seventh chord of the E♭ Major scale.

E♭ Major

6. Write the Roman numeral and figured bass for each seventh chord of the A Major scale.

A Major

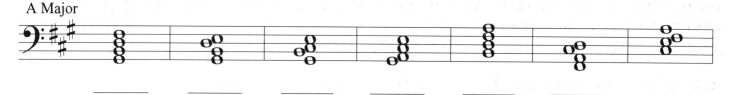

7. Draw the dominant seventh chord for each key according to the figured bass.
   (Use the harmonic form for minor keys.)

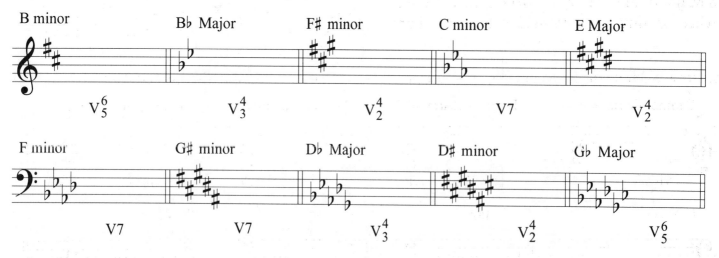

Diminished Seventh Chords

The diminished seventh chord can be built on the leading tone of the harmonic minor scale.

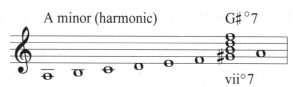

The diminished seventh chord is unique because the root, 3rd, 5th and 7th are all a minor 3rd apart. On the keyboard, the distance between the notes will not change in any inversion. The chords will "feel" the same, but will be spelled and written differently.

Any note of a diminished seventh chord can become the root by changing the spelling of the chord. Therefore, any note of a diminished seventh chord can become the leading tone of a scale. In the example below, the same diminished seventh chords as in the example above are written in root position. The root of each diminished seventh chord is functioning as a leading tone resolving to tonic.

Since any note of a diminished seventh chord can become the root, depending on the spelling of the chord, the diminished seventh chord is frequently used for modulation*. The diminished seventh chord can function like a secondary dominant** (vii°7 of V, vii°7 of IV, etc.). When used in a chord progression, vii°7 of V is usually followed by I_4^6-V7-I, as shown in the music excerpt below.

Although the diminished seventh chord can be built on the leading tone of the harmonic minor scale, diminished seventh chords are used in music in both Major and minor keys. In either a Major or minor key, accidentals must be used when writing a diminished a seventh chord.

From *Sonata, Op. 2, No. 1*, by Beethoven
(*Piano Repertoire: Baroque & Classical*, Level 10)

8. Draw a diminished seventh chord before each given chord according to the figured bass.

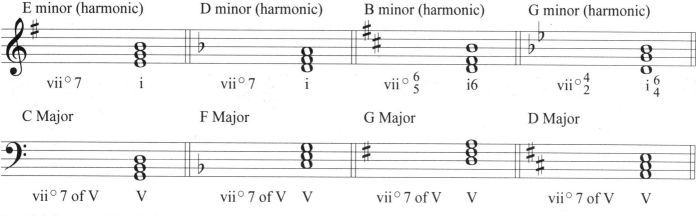

*See Unit 8.   **See Unit 7.

Unit 7
Secondary Dominant

A **secondary dominant** is the dominant of a scale degree other than the tonic. Secondary dominants are labeled with Roman numerals designating them as V of ii, V of iii, V7 of IV, etc. Secondary dominants account for most of the accidentals found in music.

1. Play this chord progression which uses secondary dominants in the key of C Major.
   Then, transpose to the keys of E♭ Major and D Major.

2. Write the Roman numerals and figured bass for these chords.

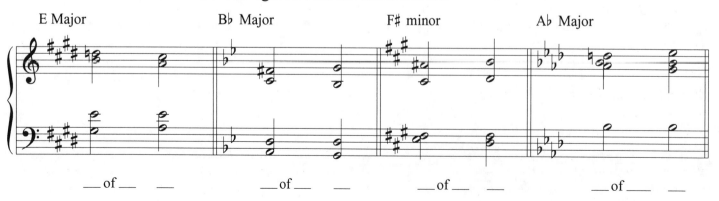

3. Write the Roman numerals and figured bass for each underlined chord in the music excerpts below.

Key of C Major

From *Sonata, K. 330* by Mozart
(*Piano Repertoire: Baroque & Classical*, Level 10)

Key of Db Major

From *Grillen* by Schumann
(*Piano Repertoire: Romantic & 20th Century*, Level 1)

From *Sonata, L. 442*, by Scarlatti
(*Piano Repertoire: Baroque & Classical*, Level 10)

Key of D minor

Unit 8
Modulation

Modulation is a change of key within a composition: one key is left and a new one is established. Most modulations occur between keys that are closely related. Closely related keys are those which are adjacent on the circle of keys. The key signatures of closely related keys differ by no more than one sharp or flat. For example, music in the key of C Major frequently modulates to G Major or F Major, or to their relative minor keys of A minor, E minor, or D minor. Recurring accidentals generally indicate a modulation.

Modulation with a Secondary Dominant

Modulation is frequently established with a **secondary dominant.** The secondary dominant becomes the dominant of the new key.

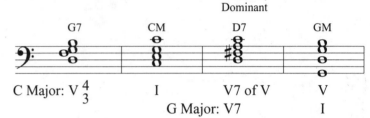

1. The music excerpts below modulate with a secondary dominant. In each music excerpt, write the Roman numerals and figured bass and name the new key. Notes in parenthesis are non-chord tones.*

From *Sonata, K. 330,* by Mozart
(*Piano Repertoire: Baroque & Classical,* Level 10)

From *Sonata, Op. 2, No. 1,* by Beethoven
(*Piano Repertoire: Baroque & Classical,* Level 10)

* See Unit 11.

Modulation with a Pivot Chord

Modulation can be established with a chord that exists in both the original key and the new key. This chord is used to **pivot** from the original key to the new key.

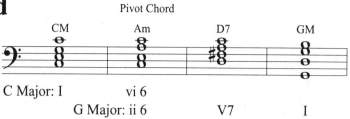

Pivot Chord

| CM | Am | D7 | GM |

C Major: I   vi 6

G Major: ii 6   V7   I

2. The music excerpts below modulate with a pivot chord. In each music excerpt, write the Roman numerals and figured bass and name the new key.

From *Sonata, Hob. XVI:34,* by Haydn
(*Piano Repertoire: Baroque & Classical*, Level 10)

E minor: _____   _____

_____ Major: _____

From *Sonata, Op. 49, No. 1* by Beethoven
(*Piano Repertoire: Baroque & Classical*, Level 8)

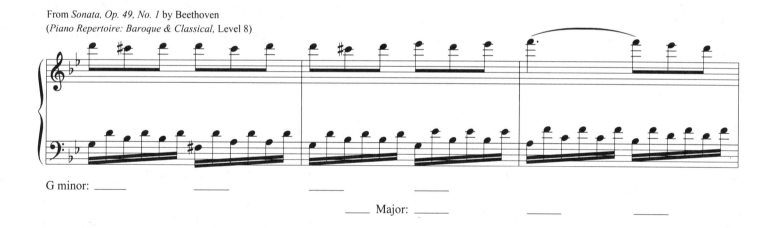

G minor: _____

_____ Major: _____

Phrase Modulation

Phrase modulation is a sudden change of key. One phrase will cadence in the original key, and the next phrase begins immediately in the new key.

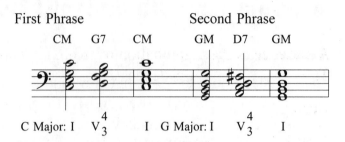

3. The music excerpts below have phrase modulations. Study the music and name the new key for each phrase. Write the Roman numerals and figured bass for the underlined chords. Notes in parenthesis are non-chord tones.*

From *Sonata, Op. 2, No. 1,* by Beethoven
(*Piano Repertoire: Baroque & Classical,* Level 10)

F minor: ____   ____

____ Major: ____   ____   ____   ____   ____

From *Sonata, Op. 2, No. 1,* by Beethoven
(*Piano Repertoire: Baroque & Classical,* Level 10)

C minor: ____   ____   ____   ____

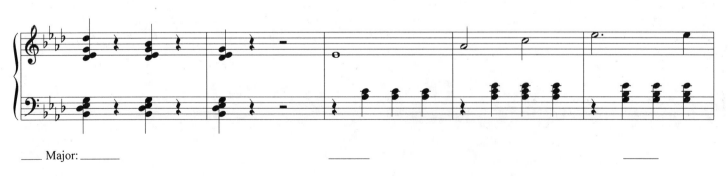

____ Major: ____   ____   ____

* See Unit 11.

Unit 9
Cadences

A **cadence** is the combination of two chords used at the end of a phrase, section, or piece of music. The various types of cadences are:

Authentic: V (or V7)-I   **Plagal:** IV-I   **Half:** any cadence ending on V (or V7)   **Deceptive:** V-vi

1. Write the Roman numerals for each chord on the lines under the staff.
   Write the name of each cadence on the line above the staff.

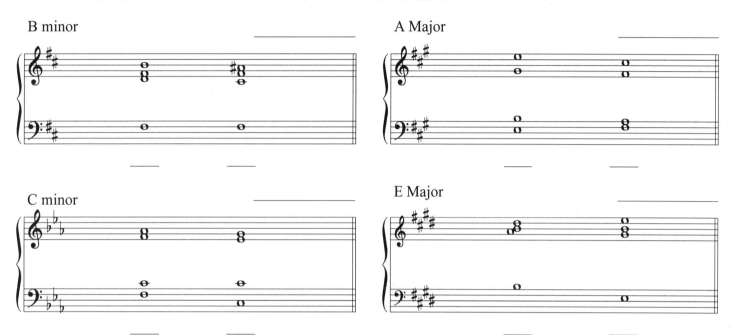

2. Write the Roman numerals for each underlined chord in the music excerpts below.
   Write the name of each cadence on the line above the staff.

From *Sonata, Op. 79,* by Beethoven
(*Piano Repertoire: Baroque & Classical,* Level 9)

From *Sonata, Op. 2, No. 1,* by Beethoven
(*Piano Repertoire: Baroque & Classical,* Level 10)

From *Etude, Op. 2, No. 1* by Scriabin
(*Piano Repertoire: Etudes,* Level 10)

From *Impromptu, Op. 90, No. 4,* by Schubert
(*Piano Repertoire: Romantic & 20th Century,* Level 10)

Unit 10
Neapolitan 6th and Augmented 6th Chords

Neapolitan 6th Chords

The **Neapolitan 6th Chord** is a Major triad built on the lowered supertonic (ii) scale degree of a Major or minor scale. The Neapolitan 6th chord is usually found in first inversion, thus the name Neapolitan "sixth". Neapolitan 6th chords are labeled **N6**. Occasionally, the Neapolitan 6th chord is found in root position. In this case, the chord is labeled **N**.

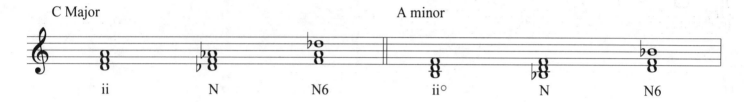

1. Draw ii, N, and N6 chords in the following keys.

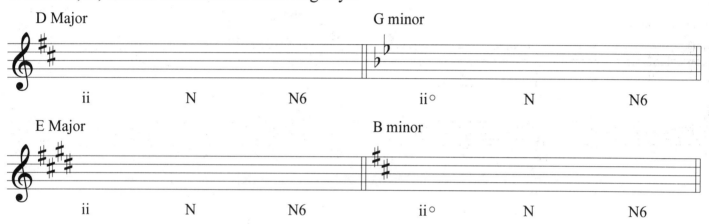

Neapolitan 6th Chords in Music

From *Bagatelle, Op. 119, No. 9* by Beethoven
(*Piano Repertoire: Baroque & Classical*, Level 3)

- The Neapolitan 6th chord generally precedes the V (or V7) chord.

- Frequently, the vii° 7 of V and/or I$_4^6$ occur between the Neapolitan 6th and the V (or V7) chords.

From *Sonata, Hob. XVI:37*, by Haydn
(*Piano Repertoire: Baroque & Classical*, Level 9)

2. Each music excerpt below has one Neapolitan 6th chord. Label the underlined chords with Roman numerals and figured bass. Label the Neapolitan 6th chord **N6** (or **N** if the chord is in root position). The notes in parenthesis are non-chord tones.*

From *Sonata, Hob. XVI:37,* by Haydn
(*Piano Repertoire: Baroque & Classical,* Level 9)

Key of D minor

___ ___ ___ of ___ ___   ___ of ___ ___ ___ ___ ___ ___

From *Prelude, Op. 28, No. 20,* by Chopin
(*Piano Repertoire: Romantic & 20th Century,* Level 7)

Key of C minor

From *Fantasy, K. 379,* by Mozart
(*Piano Repertoire: Baroque & Classical,* Level 9,)

Key of D minor

___ ___ ___   ___ of ___   ___

From *Nocturne, Op. 55, No. 1,* by Chopin
(*Piano Repertoire: Romantic & 20th Century,* Level 10)

Key of F minor

___ ___   ___ ___

* See Unit 11.

28

Augmented 6th Chords

Augmented 6th chords are built on the note that is a Major 3rd below the tonic note of a Major or minor scale and include the interval of an Augmented 6th. There are three types of Augmented 6th chords: **Italian 6th** (It6), **French 6th** (Fr6) and **German 6th** (Gr6). All three types of Augmented 6th chords have the intervals of a Major 3rd and an Augmented 6th. The French 6th chord adds the interval of an Augmented 4th. The German 6th chord adds the interval of a Perfect 5th.

- **Italian 6th:** Major 3rd + Augmented 6th (three note chord)
- **French 6th:** Major 3rd + *Augmented 4th* + Augmented 6th (four note chord)
- **German 6th:** Major 3rd + *Perfect 5th* + Augmented 6th (four note chord)

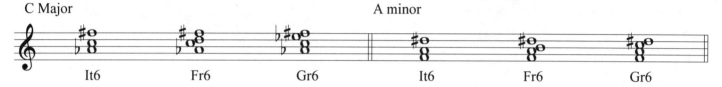

1. Draw Italian, French and German Augmented 6th chords in the following keys.

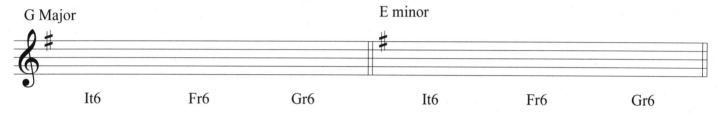

Augmented 6th Chords in Chord Progressions

Augmented 6th chords precede the V chord. The Italian 6th and French 6th may progress directly to V, or to I_4^6 then V. The German 6th must progress to I_4^6 then V. Play the chord progressions below and listen to the distinct sound of each type of Augmented 6th chord.

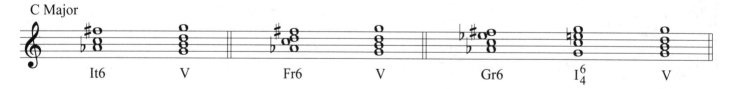

2. Draw chord progressions in the following keys as shown in the example above.

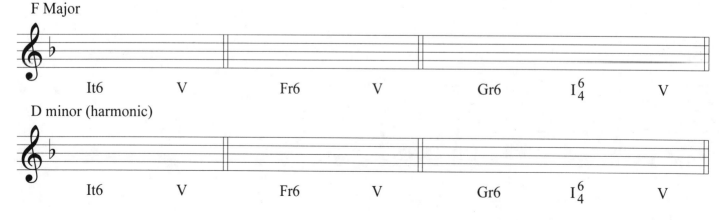

GP670

Identifying Augmented 6th Chords in Music

3. The first underlined chord in each music excerpt below is an Augmented 6th chord. Study the Augmented 6th chord in each music excerpt and determine whether it is an Italian 6th, French 6th, or German 6th. Label the chords **It6, Fr6** or **Gr6**. Name the key for each music excerpt (reminder: the bass note of each Augmented 6th chord is a Major 3rd below the tonic note of the key). Label the underlined chords that follow the Augmented 6th chords with Roman numerals and figured bass.

Key of _____

From *Waltz, Op. 33, No. 10,* by Schubert
(*Piano Repertoire: Romantic & 20th Century,* Level 8)

Key of _____

From *The Witch,* by MacDowell
(*Piano Repertoire: Romantic & 20th Century,* Level 8)

Key of _____

From *Sonata, Op. 2, No. 1,* by Beethoven
(*Piano Repertoire: Baroque & Classical,* Level 10)

From *Tarantella,* by Mendelssohn
(*Piano Repertoire: Romantic & 20th Century,* Level 7)

Key of _____

Key of _____

From *Prelude, Op. 28, No. 20,* by Chopin
(*Piano Repertoire: Romantic & 20th Century,* Level 7)

From *Rhapsody, Op. 11, No. 3,* by Dohnanyi
(*Piano Repertoire: Romantic & 20th Century,* Level 10)

Key of _____

Key of _____

From *Etude, Op. 1, No. 1,* by Liszt
(*Piano Repertoire: Etudes,* Level 10)

Key of _____

From *Sonatina, Op. 20, No. 1,* by Kuhlau
(*Piano Repertoire: Baroque & Classical,* Level 6)

Unit 11
Non-Chord Tones

Non-chord tones are notes that occur during the course of melodic movement that are not part of the chord of the moment. The various types of non-chord tones are named *passing tone, neighbor tone, anticipation, escape tone, appoggiatura, suspension* and *pedal point*. Non-chord tones that occur on rhythmically strong beats are called *accented,* and those that occur on weak beats or in between beats are called *unaccented.*

Passing Tone

A **Passing tone** (p.) is a non-chord tone that occurs between two different chord tones. It is approached and left by step without change of direction. It may be chromatic or diatonic. A passing tone may be accented or unaccented.

Neighbor Tone

A **neighbor tone** (n.) is a non-chord tone that occurs between two chord tones of the same pitch. It is approached and left by step with a change of direction. It may be chromatic or diatonic. A neighbor tone may be accented or unaccented.

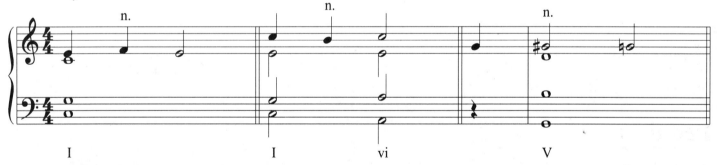

Anticipation

An **anticipation** (ant.) is a non-chord tone that occurs just before the chord to which it belongs. It is approached by step or leap and remains the same. An anticipation is an unaccented non-chord tone.

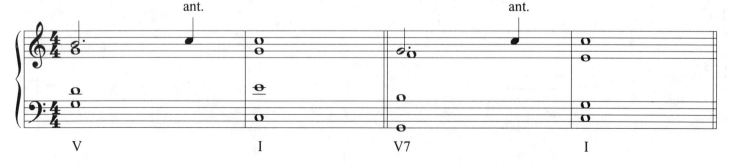

Escape Tone

An **escape tone** (e.) is a non-chord tone that occurs between two different chord tones. It is approached by step and left by leap with a change of direction. An escape tone is an unaccented non-chord tone.

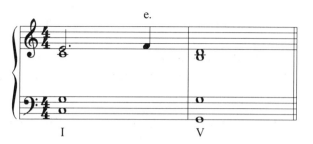

Appoggiatura

An **appoggiatura** (app.) is a non-chord tone that occurs between two different chord tones. It is approached by leap and left by step. An appoggiatura is an accented non-chord tone.

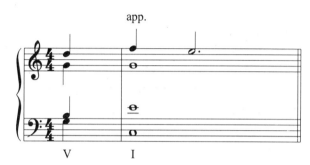

Suspension

A **suspension** (s.) is a chord tone held into a chord to which it does not belong. The three elements of a suspension are called the *preparation, suspension,* and *resolution.* The preparation is the chord tone preceding the suspension. The suspension is the same note as the preparation, but is a non-chord tone. The suspension may or may not be tied to its preparation. The resolution is the chord-tone following the suspension. The resolution is a step below the suspension. When the resolution is a step above the suspension, it is called *retardation* (r.). A suspension is an accented non-chord tone.

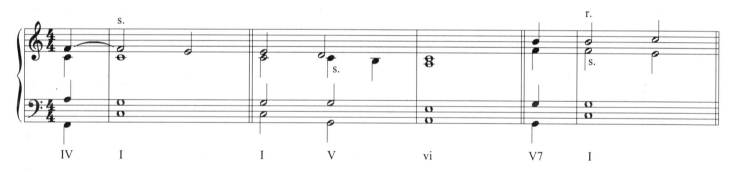

Pedal Point

A **pedal point** (ped.) begins as a chord tone, becomes a non-chord tone as harmonies change around it, and ends as a chord tone as the harmonies resolve to it. A pedal point may be accented or unaccented.

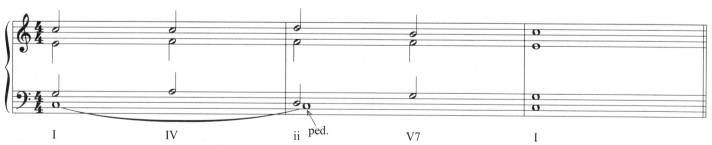

Reference Chart for Non-Chord Tones

The chart below is a summary of the melodic direction applied to each non-chord tone.

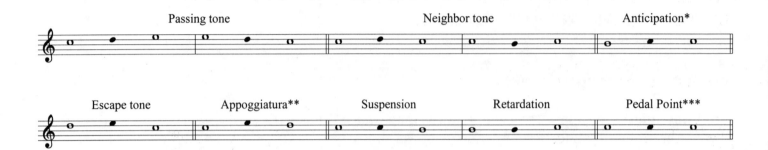

* An anticipation can be approached by step *or* leap.
** Although the appoggiatura usually resolves in the *opposite* direction to the approach, it can resolve in the *same* direction.
*** Although the pedal point usually begins as a chord tone, it can begin as a non-chord tone.

1. Write the name for each circled non-chord tone in the music excerpt below.

a) _____   b) _____   c) _____

d) _____   e) _____   f) _____

g) _____   h) _____   i) _____

From *Sonata, Op. 2, No. 1,* by Beethoven
(*Piano Repertoire: Baroque & Classical,* Level 10, page 101)

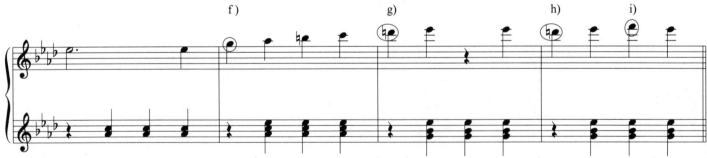

2. Write the name for each circled non-chord tone in the music excerpt below.

a) _____ b) _____ c) _____

d) _____ e) _____

From *Nocturne, Op. 55, No. 1,* by Chopin
(*Piano Repertoire: Romantic & 20th Century,* Level 10, page 27)

3. Write the name for each circled non-chord tone in the music excerpt below.

a) _____ b) _____ c) _____

d) _____ e) _____ f) _____

From *Nocturne, Op. 55, No. 1,* by Chopin
(*Piano Repertoire: Romantic & 20th Century,* Level 10, page 27)

4. Write the name for each circled non-chord tone in the music excerpt below.

a) _____ b) _____ c) _____

b) _____ e) _____ f) _____

From *French Suite No. 6 "Allemande",* by Bach
(*Piano Repertoire: Baroque & Classical,* Level 10, page 27)

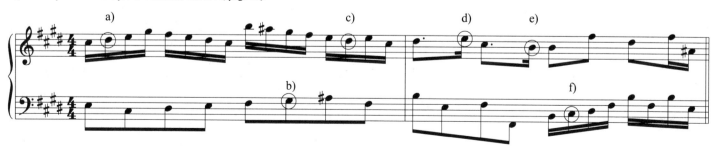

Unit 12
Fugue

Fugue is the most highly evolved style of imitative polyphonic music from the Baroque period. A fugue may have two or more voices; however, fugues with three or four voices are the most common. The fugue was brought to perfection by Johann Sebastian Bach (1685-1750).

Melodic Elements

- **Subject:** Fugues are based on a short melody called the subject. The subject is stated at the beginning of the fugue in one voice and is immediately imitated by the other voices. The subject will be stated many times throughout the fugue in all the voices.

- **Answer:** The imitation of the subject in another key, usually the dominant, is called the answer. Answers may be real or tonal. A real answer is an exact transposition of the subject. A tonal answer has modified intervals.

- **Countersubject:** The countersubject is a contrasting melody that is stated in the first voice immediately after the subject as the second voice imitates the subject. The countersubject may be derived from motives in the subject or may be a continuation of the subject. The countersubject will be stated many times throughout the fugue in all the voices.

Compositional Devices

- **Imitation:** Imitation is the immediate restatement of a subject or motive in another voice.

- **Sequence:** A sequence occurs when a subject or motive is repeated in the same voice at a higher or lower pitch.

- **Inversion:** A subject or motive is inverted when ascending intervals are changed into the corresponding descending intervals and vice versa (i.e.: *up a 2nd - up a 2nd - down a 3rd* becomes *down a 2nd - down a 2nd - up a 3rd*).

Fugue Structure

Although the fugue does not have an exact form, there are basic principles and characteristics in the structure of a fugue. The overall structure of a fugue is the imitation of a subject and a countersubject (or derived motives) in alternating sections called expositions and episodes.

- **Exposition:** A section in which the subject is stated at least once in each voice is called an exposition. A fugue may have one or many expositions. The term exposition is sometimes used only for the first exposition, without any special name for later sections of similar construction. Later expositions usually involve modulations to other keys such as the relative minor, dominant, or subdominant, with a return to the tonic key in the last exposition.

- **Episode:** A section of the fugue that does not include a statement of the subject is called an episode. The exposition sections are separated from one another by episodes. Episodes are usually based on motives from the subject or countersubject. These motives are frequently used in sequences. The episodes, although still in strict polyphonic style, are somewhat freer in structure than expositions.

- **Stretto:** A section of a fugue in which the imitation of the subject occurs in close succession, with the answer entering before the complete statement of the subject is called a stretto. This overlapping of the subject and its imitation creates an increased intensity that is particularly effective at the end of a fugue.

The Well-Tempered Clavier by J. S. Bach

The Well-Tempered Clavier (Das Wohltemperierte Clavier)* is a collection of forty-eight preludes and fugues by J. S. Bach, published in two volumes (1722 and 1744), each of which contains twenty-four preludes and fugues, one for each Major and minor key. The fugues found on pages 36-39 are from the first volume of *The Well-Tempered Clavier.*

Answer these questions about the Fugue in C Minor on pages 36-37.

1. How many voices are in this fugue? _____

2. Is the answer in measure 3 real or tonal? _____

3. Name the compositional device used in measures 5-6. _____

4. In what measure does the third voice enter with the subject? _____

5. In what measure does the first exposition end? _____

6. Name the compositional device used in measures 9-11. _____

7. Is the motive in the right hand in measures 9-11 from the subject or countersubject? _____

8. Is the motive in the left hand in measures 9-11 from the subject or countersubject? _____

9. How many complete statements of the subject are found in measures 11-31? _____

Answer these questions about the Fugue in D Minor on pages 38-39.

10. How many voices are in this fugue? _____

11. Is the answer in measure 3 real or tonal? _____

12. In what measure does the third voice enter with the subject? _____

13. Name the compositional device used in measures 9-11. _____

14. Name the compositional device used in the right hand in measures 22-23. _____

15. What is the term for the structure of measures 21-23? _____

16. Name the compositional device used in the left hand in measures 23-24. _____

17. Name the compositional device used in measures 31-32. _____

18. How many complete statements of the subject are found in measures 39-41? _____

19. What is the term for the structure of measures 39-41? _____

*The name refers to the then new system of tuning called equal temperament, which made it possible to play equally well in all keys.

Fugue in C Minor

WTC Book 1, No. 2

J. S. Bach
(1685-1750)

Fugue in D Minor

WTC Book 1, No. 6

J. S. Bach
(1685-1750)

Unit 13
Suite

The **suite** is an important form of Baroque keyboard music that consists of a number of movements, each in the character of a dance and all in the same key. The standard scheme of dance movements in a suite is (1) allemande, (2) courante, (3) sarabande, (4) optional dance or group of dances such as the minuet, bourreé, polonaise and gavotte, (5) gigue. The dance movements are always in binary form, either symmetrical (both sections approximately the same length) or asymmetrical with the second section lengthened in a way that foreshadows sonata-allegro form.

The Four Standard Dance Movements

The four standard dance movements in a suite are the allemande, courante, sarabande and gigue. These dances originated in the 16th century and are older than the optional dance types. By the time they were adopted into the suite in the 17th century, these dances became stylized and lost much of their original dance essence.

1) **Allemande** (F.): The allemande is in moderate 4/4 time with a short upbeat (usually one sixteenth note). The allemande features continuous sixteenth note passages that are imitated in the various voices creating a basically polyphonic texture. The dance originated from the German *alman*. In the 17th century the allemande was regularly used as the first movement of a suite.

From *French Suite No.6* by Bach
(*Piano Repertoire: Baroque & Classical,* Level 10, page 27)

2) **Courante** (F.) or *corrente,* (It.): The courante is generally characterized by a light texture with rapid figures. The courante became stylized as two types: the French courante and the Italian corrente. The Italian corrente is in quick triple time (usually 3/4) with running passages. The French courante is in a moderate 3/2 or 6/4 time with frequent shifts from one of these meters to the other. In most courantes, the change from 3/2 to 6/4 occurs at the final measure of each section. The courante is in polyphonic texture with the melodic material alternating between the upper and lower voices. In the 17th century the courante became a standard movement of the suite. The courantes in suites by J. S. Bach are usually the French type. In early editions of suites by Bach the distinction between correntes and courantes is correctly indicated, however later editions have substituted the name courante for many or all of the correntes.

From *French Suite No. 6* by Bach
(*Piano Repertoire: Baroque & Classical,* Level 10, page 30)

From *English Suite No.3* by Bach

Courante

3) **Sarabande** (F.; Sp. *zarabanda*): The sarabande is a Spanish dance in slow triple meter and dignified style, usually without upbeat and frequently with an accent or prolonged note on the second beat. The sarabande probably came from Mexico and appeared in Spain in the 16th century. In the 17th century, the sarabande appeared in France and England and became a standard movement of the suite.

From *French Suite No. 6* by Bach
(*Piano Repertoire: Baroque & Classical,* Level 10, page 32)

Sarabande

4) **Gigue** (F.; It. *giga*): The gigue evolved from the Irish or English jig and developed differently in France and Italy. The French type is characterized by compound meter (usually 6/8), quick tempo, and polyphonic texture of imitative or fugal style. The less common Italian type (giga) is faster (presto), nonfugal, with running passages over a harmonic basis. The gigue is usually the final movement in suites of the 17th century. The gigues in suites by Bach are usually of the French type.

From *French Suite No. 6* by Bach
(*Piano Repertoire: Baroque & Classical,* Level 10, page 39)

Gigue

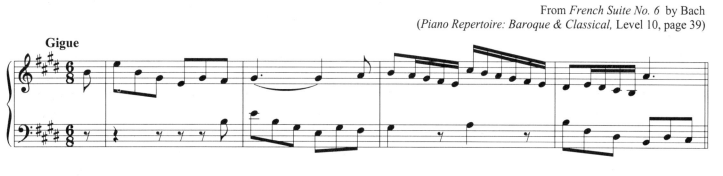

From *English Suite No. 2* by Bach

Giga

Optional Dance Movements

The optional dances create a contrast to the standard dances by being simpler in style and more clearly suggestive of dance types. The optional dances originated in the ballet of the 17th century and retained the character of actual dance music.

Bourreé (F.): The bourreé is a French dance, usually in quick duple meter beginning with a single (one quarter note) upbeat. It was originally used in ballets and operas, and then incorporated into suites of the 17th century.

From *French Suite No. 6* by Bach
(*Piano Repertoire: Baroque & Classical,* Level 10, page 36)

Bourreé

Gavotte (F.): The gavotte is a French dance in moderate 4/4 time with an upbeat of two quarter notes and phrases generally ending and beginning in the middle of a measure. The gavotte became popular in the 17th century when it was introduced into ballets and operas. Bach frequently used it as one of the optional dance movements in his keyboard suites.

From *French Suite No. 6* by Bach
(*Piano Repertoire: Baroque & Classical,* Level 10, page 34)

Gavotte

Minuet (F. *menuet*; G. *menuett*; It. *minuetto*): The minuet is a French country dance in 3/4 time, in moderate tempo. The first minuet was introduced at the court of King Louis XIV around 1650 and was soon adopted as the official court dance. As a result, it spread quickly throughout Europe and superceded older dance types, thereby establishing a new period of dance and dance music. The minuet was the only Baroque dance type that did not become obsolete after the decline of the suite (around 1750). Two minuets are frequently included in suites to be played in the order of minuet 1 - minuet 2 - minuet 1, which was the origin of the minuet and trio movement found in many sonatas of the classical period.

From *French Suite No. 6* by Bach
(*Piano Repertoire: Baroque & Classical,* Level 10, page 38)

Minuet

Polonaise (F.): The polonaise is a Polish dance of festive and stately character. The music is always in moderate triple meter, has phrases without upbeat, and generally includes measures with a short repeated rhythmic motive. The earliest known examples of polonaises with these characteristics are found in the suites of Bach. In the 19th century, the polonaise acquired its classic form, which, in addition to the features mentioned above, is characterized by the rhythmic pattern:

From *French Suite No.6* by Bach
(*Piano Repertoire: Baroque & Classical,* Level 10, page 35)

Polonaise

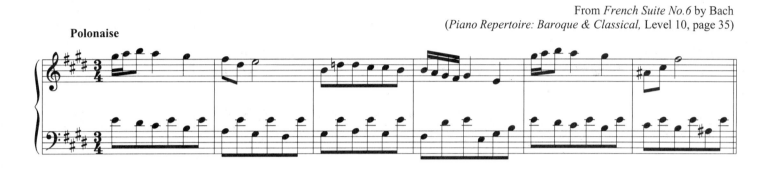

Study the music excerpts below and determine the correct dance name for each. Write the name on the line above the staff.

1. _____   From *Paritita No. 1* by Bach

2. _____   From *Suite in A* by Teleman

3. _____   From *English Suite No. 2* by Bach

4. _____   From *English Suite No. 3* by Bach

5. _____   by Telemann

6. _____   From *French Suite No. 3* by Bach

GP670

Unit 14
Rondo Form

Music in **rondo form** has a recurring section (A) that alternates with contrasting sections (B, C, etc.). The recurring section is called the **rondo theme,** and the alternating sections are called **episodes**. The rondo theme is repeated one to four times throughout the piece, usually in the tonic key, and sometimes with modifications. Episodes appear between statements of the rondo theme, and are usually in contrasting keys. A typical rondo form is:

> A. Rondo theme (tonic key)
> B. Episode 1 (dominant, subdominant, relative, or parallel key)
> A. Rondo theme (tonic key)
> C. Episode 2 (dominant, subdominant, relative, or parallel key)
> A. Rondo theme (tonic key)

A **transition** is occasionally used to connect the rondo theme to an episode or an episode to the return of the rondo theme. A transition generally prepares a modulation to the key of the upcoming episode or returning rondo theme. Transitions may use motives from an episode, the rondo theme, or both.

Rondo form was developed and perfected in music of the Classical period (1750-1825). Rondos are frequently found as final movements in sonatas by Haydn, Mozart and Beethoven.

The rondo on pages 45-47 is the 3rd movement of the *Sonata, Hob. XVI:37* by Joseph Haydn (1732-1809). The first and second statements of the rondo theme and episode 1 are marked for you in the music. Study the music to complete the questions below.

1. In what Major key is the rondo theme? _____

2. In what key is episode 1? (circle one)   Relative minor

   Parallel minor

3. In what measure does episode 2 begin? Write *C: Episode 2* above this measure. _____

4. In what key is episode 2?   Dominant

   Subdominant

5. In what measure does the third statement of the rondo theme begin?
   Write *A: Rondo Theme* above this measure.   _____

6. Which statement of the rondo theme has modifications: first, second or third? _____

7. After which episode is there a transition?   Episode 1

   Episode 2

8. In what measure does the transition begin? Write *transition* above this measure. _____

Finale:Rondo
from Sonata, Hob. XVI:37

Joseph Haydn
(1732-1809)

A: Rondo Theme

B: Episode 1

A: Rondo Theme

Unit 15
Theme and Variations

Theme and variations is a form in which a musical theme is followed by any number of modified restatements. Each modified restatement of the theme is called a variation. Theme and variations appear as independent works or as a movement of a sonata.

Theme

The theme is usually in binary form, 16-32 measures long and frequently borrowed from another composer. The theme always has a distinct melody and a definite ending.

Variations

Fixed Elements. The features that a variation has in common with the theme are called fixed elements. These fixed elements may be categorized into three types of variation:

1) A variation that preserves both the melody and harmony of a theme.
2) A variation that preserves the essential harmony of a theme.
3) A variation in which the harmonies deviate, but the over-all structure is preserved, such as the as the number of measures, the structure of sections and phrases, and the location of cadences.

Variable Elements. The ways in which themes are varied are called variable elements. A theme may be varied with one or more of the following variable elements:

a) Melodic variation: embellishment of the original melody, or a new melody
b) Harmonic variation: deviation from the original harmony
c) Parallel key variation: a shift from a Major key to the parallel minor or vice versa
d) Motivic variation: a distinct motive is used throughout a variation (melodic or rhythmic)
e) Tempo variation: change of tempo
f) Meter variation: change of time signature
g) Texture variation: change from homophonic to polyphonic texture or vice versa. A change to polyphonic texture may include the use of imitative, fugal, or canonic styles.

From *12 Variations on "Ah, vous dirai-je, Maman"* by Mozart
(*Piano Repertoire: Baroque & Classical,* Level 7, pages 26-39)

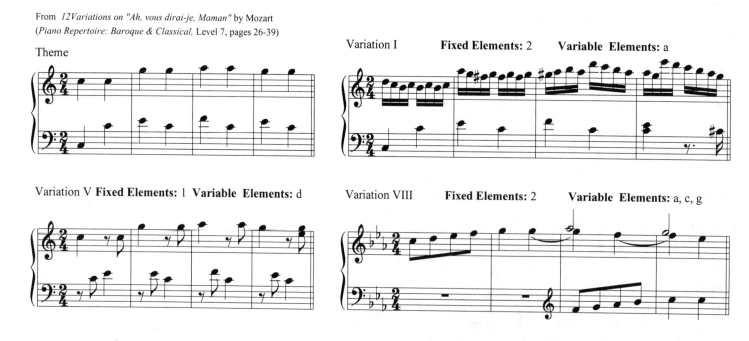

1. Study the theme and variations excerpt below. Identify each type of variation (1, 2 or 3) by determining the fixed elements. Then, identify the variable elements (a, b, c, etc.) in each variation.

From *Six Variations on a Swiss Song,* by Beethoven
(*Piano Repertoire: Baroque & Classical,* Level 6, page 40)

Theme

Variation II   **Fixed Elements:** _____   **Variable Elements:** _____

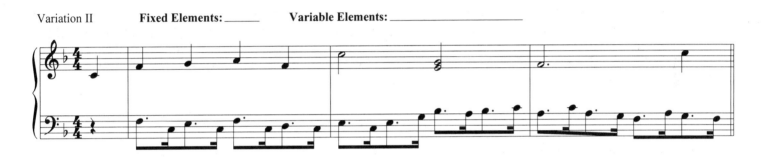

Variation III   **Fixed Elements:** _____   **Variable Elements:** _____

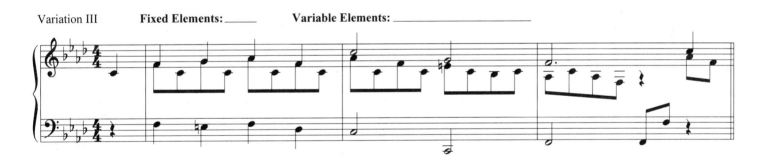

Variation I   **Fixed Elements:** _____   **Variable Elements:** _____

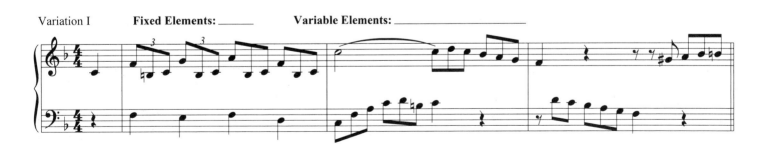

2. Study the theme and variations excerpt below. Identify each type of variation (1, 2 or 3) by determining the fixed elements. Then, identify the variable elements (a, b, c, etc.) in each variation.

From *Six Variations on "Nel con piu non mi sento"* (Paisiello), by Beethoven

Theme

Variation I   **Fixed Elements:** _____   **Variable Elements:** _____

Variation III   **Fixed Elements:** _____   **Variable Elements:** _____

Variation IV   **Fixed Elements:** _____   **Variable Elements:** _____

3. Study the theme and variations excerpt below. Identify each type of variation (1, 2 or 3) by determining the fixed elements. Then, identify the variable elements (a, b, c, etc.) in each variation.

From *12 Variations on "Ah, vous dirai-je, Maman"* by Mozart
(*Piano Repertoire: Baroque & Classical,* Level 7, page 26)

Theme

Variation XI **Fixed Elements:** _____ **Variable Elements:** _____

Variation XII   **Fixed Elements:** _____   **Variable Elements:** _____

4. Study the theme and variations excerpt below. Identify each type of variation (1, 2 or 3) by determining the fixed elements. Then, identify the variable elements (a, b, c, etc.) in each variation.

From *Variations and Fugue on a Theme by Handel,* by Brahms
Theme

Variation VI   **Fixed Elements:** _____   **Variable Elements:** _____

Variation XIX   **Fixed Elements:** _____   **Variable Elements:** _____

leggiero e vivace

Unit 16
Sonata-Allegro Form

First movements of sonatas are usually written in a form called **sonata-allegro** or *first movement* form*. Sonata-allegro became the most important form of the Classical period and was brought to its highest level of sophistication in the sonatas by Haydn, Mozart and Beethoven.

Sonata-allegro is a ternary form. The three sections of sonata-allegro form are shown below.

1. **Exposition**
   A. First theme: tonic key
   B. Second theme: dominant key, or relative Major key if the movement is in a minor key.
   C. Closing theme (optional): dominant key, or relative Major if the movement is in a minor key.

2. **Development**
   Themes (and/or motives from themes) are presented in new keys.
   New themes may be added.

3. **Recapitulation**
   A. First theme: tonic key
   B. Second theme: tonic key
   C. Closing theme (optional): tonic key

A **coda** (ending) is sometimes included after the second theme or closing theme.

The music on pages 53-57 is the first movement of the *Sonata, Hob. XVI:34* by Joseph Haydn (1732-1809). Study the music to answer the following questions.

1. In what minor key does the First Theme begin? _____

2. To what Major key does the First Theme modulate at measure 14? _____

3. In what key is the Second Theme? _____

4. Which theme is used in the Development: First or Second? _____

5. Name the minor key used in measures 46-50. _____

6. Name the Major key used in measures 51-54. _____

7. Name the minor key used in measures 60-71. _____

8. In the Recapitulation, does the First Theme modulate or remain in the tonic key? _____

9. In what key is the Second Theme in the Recapitulation? _____

10. Provide a harmonic analysis of the music by writing Roman numerals and figured bass on the lines under the staffs according to the keys that you have named in questions 1-9.

*The term first movement form, although correctly and frequently used, is somewhat misleading because sonata-allegro form is not limited to first movements. Sonata movements other than the first are sometimes written in sonata-allegro form. Sonata-allegro form is also used in symphonies and concertos.

Sonata

Hob. XVI:34
(First movement)

Joseph Haydn
(1732-1809)

EXPOSITION

First Theme

___ Minor: _____
(tonic key)

_____ of _____
(boxed chord)

___ of ___ _____

___ Major: _____
(new key)

Second Theme

Closing Theme

DEVELOPMENT

___ Minor: ___
(new key)

___ Major: ___
(new key)

_____ Minor: _____
(new key)

RECAPITULATION
First Theme

_____ Minor: _____
(tonic key)

Closing Theme

Coda

Unit 17
Tonality in the 20th Century

Extended Tertian Harmony

Tertian harmony is the system of building chords in thirds, such as triads and seventh chords. **Extended tertian harmony** is the use of additional thirds above the 7th, resulting in 9th, 11th, and 13th chords.

Key of C Major

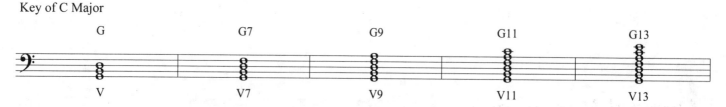

Ninth, 11th and 13th chords are used most often as dominant harmonies in Major or minor keys: V9, V11, or V13. These chords can also be used as secondary dominants: V9 of V, V11 of V, V13 of V, etc. Ninth, 11th and 13th chords are generally found in root position with the 9th, 11th or 13th in an upper voice. All of the notes of the chords are rarely present.

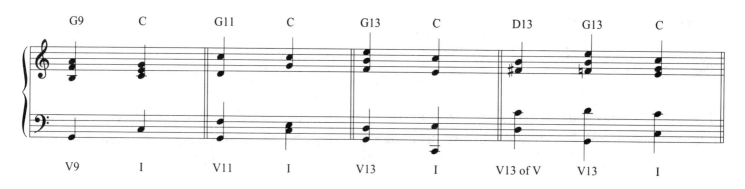

In music of the Baroque and Classical periods (1600-1825), 9th, 11th and 13th chords are extremely rare. The added 9th, 11th and 13th notes are generally considered non-chord tones. Although relatively rare in the Romantic period (1825-1900), added 9th, 11th and 13th notes began to be accepted as chord tones. Ninth, 11th and 13th chords became widely used in music of the Late Romantic and Impressionist periods (1875-1920) and are used extensively in jazz and popular music throughout the 20th century.

From *Preludium* by MacDowell
(*Piano Repertoire: Romantic & 20th Century*, Level 10)

From *Yesterdays and Tomorrows* by Larry Minsky
(*Patterns of Jazz: Jazz Piano*, Level 6)

1. Draw a dominant 9th, 11th or 13th chord as indicated by the chord symbol and figured bass.

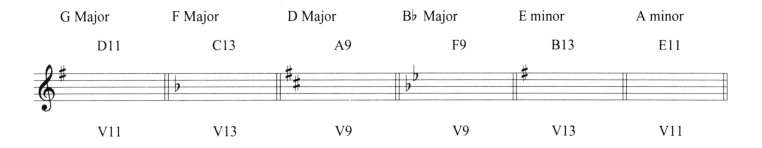

Quartal Harmony

Quartal Harmony is a system of building chords in fourths rather than the more commonly used tertian system. Quartal chords built in perfect fourths with 3, 4 or 5 notes are considered consonant.* Quartal chords that include Augmented fourths, or six or more notes are considered dissonant.*

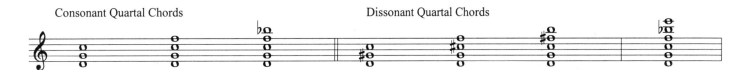

The use of quartal harmony is common in music of the 20th century. However, it is rare for an entire composition to only use quartal harmony. Music that is predominantly quartal often includes chords with intervals other than fourths, creating a mixture of quartal and tertian harmony.

From *Rhapsody* by Jeanine Yeager

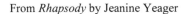

*Consonance and dissonance are terms used to describe the perceived pleasant or unpleasant effect of the various intervals. Thirds, sixths, perfect fourths, perfect fifths and octaves are generally considered to be consonant. Seconds, Augmented fourths, diminished fifths and sevenths are generally considered to be dissonant.

Polytonality, Bitonality and Atonality

Polytonality is the use of two or more keys at the same time. However, the use of more than two keys at the same time is extremely rare.

Bitonality is the use of two different keys at the same time. Bitonality it a specific type of polytonality. Bitonality may be accomplished with two key signatures, or with the use of accidentals. An entire composition may be bitonal, or only a section.

In the music excerpt below, two key signatures are used at the same time. This entire piece is bitonal.

From *Bagatelle No. 1* by Bartok

In the music excerpt below, accidentals are used to create a bitonal section of this piece. The left hand plays diatonic triads in C Major, while the right hand plays broken chords that have accidentals alluding to a contrasting key.

From ... *Brouillards* by Debussy

Atonality is the avoidance of any key or tonal center. Atonality is generally associated with extremely dissonant music, however some composers successfully diffuse any sense of tonal center or key while still employing tertian based harmonies.

In the first music excerpt below, dissonant harmonic and melodic intervals are used to avoid any implication of key or tonal center. In the second music excerpt below, a series of unrelated triads are used to completely diffuse any sense of key or tonal center.

From *Bagatelle No. 2* by Bartok

From ...*Canope* by Debussy

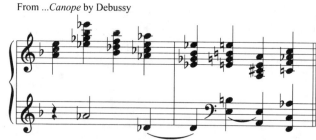

2. Match each term with its definition.

      a. Bitonality   _____ Two or more keys at the same time

      b. Quartal Harmony   _____ Avoidance of any key or tonal center

      c. Polytonality   _____ Ninth, 11th, and 13th chords

      d. Atonality   _____ Two different keys at the same time

      e. Extended tertian harmony   _____ Chords built in fourths

3. Identify each music excerpt as extended tertian harmony, quartal harmony, bitonality or atonality.

Serialism and the 12 Tone Row

Serialism in music is the use of musical elements (such as pitches, rhythm, dynamics, articulations, etc.) to organize or *serialize* the structure of a composition. The serialization of the selected element(s) supercedes the traditional concepts of key relationships and thematic development as the most important means for creating form and structure in serial music.

12 Tone Row is a serial technique that uses the twelve notes of the chromatic scale in a fixed order chosen by the composer. Except for immediate repetitions, no note may be repeated until the other eleven have appeared. The notes of the row may appear with enharmonic spellings as the piece progresses. The fixed order of the chosen 12 tone row may appear in one of the four forms shown below.

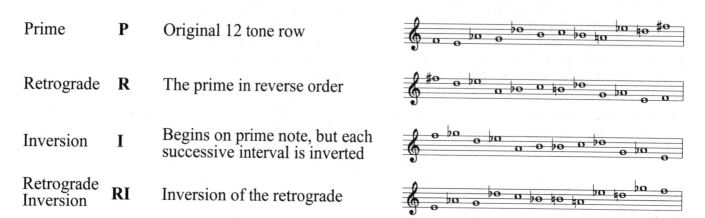

Prime	**P**	Original 12 tone row	
Retrograde	**R**	The prime in reverse order	
Inversion	**I**	Begins on prime note, but each successive interval is inverted	
Retrograde Inversion	**RI**	Inversion of the retrograde	

Any of the forms of a row may be transposed. A *matrix* is used to organize the transpositions of a row. In the matrix below, the shaded rows are the untransposed forms of the 12 tone row shown in the examples above. The remaining rows are transpositions beginning on each note of the untransposed row forms.

P: read left to right   **R:** read right to left   **I:** read top to bottom   **RI:** read bottom to top

Inversion transpositions →

	I	I	I	I	I	I	I	I	I	I	I	I	
P	F	E	Ab	G	C#	B	C	Bb	A	Eb	D	F#	**R**
P	Gb	F	A	Ab	D	C	Db	B	Bb	E	Eb	G	**R**
P	D	Db	F	E	Bb	Ab	A	G	Gb	C	B	Eb	**R**
P	Eb	D	Gb	F	B	A	Bb	Ab	G	Db	C	E	**R**
P	A	Ab	C	B	F	E	Eb	D	Db	G	F#	Bb	**R**
P	B	Bb	D	Db	G	F	F#	E	Eb	A	Ab	C	**R**
P	Bb	A	Db	C	Gb	E	F	Eb	D	Ab	G	B	**R**
P	C	B	Eb	D	Ab	Gb	G	F	E	Bb	A	Db	**R**
P	Db	C	E	Eb	A	G	Ab	F#	F	B	Bb	D	**R**
P	G	F#	Bb	A	Eb	Db	D	C	B	F	E	Ab	**R**
P	Ab	G	Bb	B	E	D	Eb	Db	C	F#	F	A	**R**
P	E	Eb	G	Gb	C	Bb	B	A	Ab	D	Db	F	**R**
	RI	RI	RI	RI	RI	RI	RI	RI	RI	RI	RI	RI	**R**

Prime transpositions (left) — Retrograde transpositions (right)

← Retrograde inversion transpositions →

Arnold Schoenberg (1874-1951) invented the 12 tone row technique around 1920 out of his desire to organize chromatic atonal music into a coherent musical language. Like many composers of the early 20th century, Schoenberg was looking for ways to break free from the traditional concepts of tonality in music.

4. The music below is written with a 12 tone row. The 12 tone row used in this piece is the row shown in the examples and matrix on page 62. The row is used six times throughout the piece in various forms. The beginning of each row is marked for you with a number. Rows 1, 2, 4, 5, and 6 are untransposed row forms (shaded rows in the matrix). Row 3 is a transposed row form. Study the music and use the matrix to determine the form of the row each time it appears. Write the name of each row form on the lines below (prime, inversion, retrograde or retrograde inversion). Reminder: enharmonic spellings may be used for any row note.

1._____

2._____

Additional guidelines for analyzing a 12 tone row piece:

3._____

- A note may be repeated immediately after it appears in the row
- A note may be sustained while the row continues
- Adjacent row notes may be played as harmonic intervals
- The notes of the row may appear in any register

4._____

5._____

6._____

Aufgeben Stück

Unit 18
The Four Periods of Music History

The history of music writing is generally divided into four basic periods: (1) Baroque, (2) Classical, (3) Romantic, and (4) 20th Century. Each period has certain styles which make it unique.

1. The Baroque Period (1600-1750)

The era from approximately 1600 to 1750 is known as the Baroque period. The term *baroque* was originally used to describe a style of art and architecture of highly decorative and extravagant design. The aesthetic ideal of the Baroque period permeated all aspects of European culture. Theater, painting, architecture and music were all characterized by grandiose concepts, dazzling effects, ornate design, and an overall dramatic quality.

Historical Context. Important historical events of the Baroque period were the Thirty Years War in Germany (1618-1648), the reign of Louis the XIV of France (1643-1715), the English Civil War (1642-1649), and the Restoration (1660). It was a time of worldwide colonization. Important names in science were Newton and Galileo. The leading philosophers were Descartes and Pascal. Prominent artists of the period include Dutch painters Rembrandt and Van Dyck, and the Spanish painter El Greco. The literature from the period include works by English writers Milton, Defoe, Addison, Swift, and Samuel Johnson, and French writers Racine and Moliere.

Baroque Music. Changes in style and form occurred continuously during the Baroque period, yet certain trends set Baroque music apart from that of other periods.

Basso Continuo. The lowest part in most Baroque music is the *basso continuo* (also called *thoroughbass*). It functions both as a melodic and harmonic bass. The basso continuo part is written in the bass staff with figured bass below the notes. It was the performer's responsibility to fill in the harmony according to the figured bass. This process is called *realizing* the figured bass.

Harmony. Figured bass reflected new harmonic concepts in music. Chords and inversions, authentic cadences, and chromaticism acquired a prominent role. Modulation and the use of seventh chords became commonplace.

Tonality. The Baroque period saw the maturation of the modern concepts of Major and minor tonality. Titles of compositions began to indicate keys (Sonata in D minor, Suite in A Major, etc.) and music began to convey a strong sense of tonal center.

Texture. The texture of Baroque music is predominantly polyphonic. The polyphony is harmonically oriented, and it reached its highest level of mastery in the music of Johann Sebastian Bach. The relative prominence of the bass line is also an aspect of Baroque texture. Homophonic texture exists in certain types of Baroque music where a single melodic line is supported by harmonic material.

Tempo and Dynamics. For the first time in history, some composers began to use tempo and dynamic markings in an attempt to convey the correct expression, emotional content or mood of the music. However, tempo and dynamic markings were limited and not used by all composers.

Improvisation. Improvisation played an important role in the performance of Baroque music. Musicians were highly trained in the art of improvising melodic ornaments, variations on a theme, cadenzas, and the realization of figured bass with complex polyphonic material.

Musical Forms. The most important form that evolved during the Baroque period was the *fugue*. The dance suite was also a prominent form developed during the Baroque period. Dance suite movements were most frequently in binary form. Additional styles of Baroque keyboard pieces include the *invention*, *prelude*, and *toccata*.

Baroque Composers

Bach, Johann Sebastian (Germany, 1685-1750)

Couperin, François (France, 1668-1733)

Daquin, Louis (France, 1694-1772)

Handel, George Frideric (b. Germany 1685-d. England 1759)

Rameau, Jean-Philippe (France, 1683-1764)

Scarlatti, Domenico (b. Italy 1685 - d.Spain 1757)

Telemann, Georg Philipp (Germany, 1681-1767)

Baroque Keyboard Instruments. Precursors of the modern piano are the *clavichord* and *harpsichord*. The clavichord mechanism produced a tone by means of a small metal tangent attached to the end of the key which struck the strings from below. The tone was delicate and the instrument was used mostly in intimate settings. The harpsichord became the "concert grand" of the 18th century. The tone of this plucked keyboard instrument was fuller and had more carrying power than that of the clavichord. An early version of the harpsichord was constructed in 1503 by Giovanni Spinetti of Venice. Named after its inventor, the *spinet* (called the *virginal* in England) produced a tone by plucking the string with a quill. In France, the harpsichord was called the *clavecin*, and in Italy, the *cembalo* or *clavicembalo*. Later harpsichord makers added longer strings and various stops and pedals. By the mid-17th century harpsichords had two keyboards, with two or three strings for each pitch to produce a fuller tone.

Baroque composers adapted their compositions to the capabilities of the clavichord and harpsichord. Since the harpsichord was unable to produce gradual tone gradations (crescendos and diminuendos), composers wrote "echo" effects: a phrase played loud on one keyboard and then repeated softly on a second keyboard. The juxtaposition of loud and soft dynamics is called *terraced dynamics*. Because of the lack of sustaining power, especially of the harpsichord, numerous embellishments were added to "fill-in" the sound. Through the use of various stops and coupling or dampening of the strings a variety of effects could be made.

2. The Classical Period (1750-1825)

The 18th century encompasses several stylistic trends which overlap chronologically. It includes the diverse musical concepts of style and form of the late Baroque, Pre-Classical, and Classical periods. The years from 1750 to 1825 represent the rise and culmination of classicism in music.

Historical Context. The years from 1750 to 1825 were marked by the rise of democratic forces manifested in the French Revolution. Other military conflicts were the Seven Years' War (1756-1763), the French and Indian Wars in America, the conflict between England and the American colonies culminating in the Declaration of Independence (1776) and the American Revolution, the War of 1812, and the Napoleonic Wars in Europe. Important writers of the time include Voltaire and Rousseau. Artists of the period include Watteau, Goya, David, Gainsborough, and Copley. Achievements in science were the development of the first vaccine, the discoveries of oxygen, hydrogen, electromagnetic induction, and ultraviolet rays. The invention of the steam engine, cotton gin, electric motors and generators were factors in the Industrial Revolution, which began in England around 1760.

Pre-Classical Music. Music which represents the transition from the Baroque to Classical period is usually called Pre-Classical. Changes in concepts of form and style took place from approximately 1720 to 1750. No clear line of separation can be drawn between late Baroque, Pre-classical and early Classical music. A variety of styles often occur in works of the same composer. Basic changes include the abandonment of polyphonic texture in favor of homophonic texture, the disappearance of the basso continuo, and binary form replaced with ternary form.

Pre-Classical Composers

Bach, Johann Christian (Germany, 1735-1782)   Kirnberger, Johann Philipp (Germany, 1721-1783)
Bach, Carl Philipp Emanuel (Germany, 1714-1788)   Mozart, Leopold (Austria, 1719-1787)
Bach, Wilhelm Friedemann (Germany, 1710-1784)   Paradisi, Domenico (Italy, 1707-1791)
Benda, Georg (Germany, 1722-1795)

Classical Music. The word *classical* may be defined with three contrasting meanings: (1) the art and literature of ancient Greece, (2) the antonym of "popular" music, and (3) the era from approximately 1750 to 1825. It is the third definition that is used in music history. Classicism implies the ideals of the Apollonian cult of ancient Greece: objectivity, ethos, emotional restraint, and the balance and clarity of form. These ideals are reflected in the music of the Classical period.

Form. Ternary forms, particularly sonata-allegro form, were firmly established during the Classical period. Phrase structure was characteristically clear with well defined cadences, and phrases were shorter (usually four measures) than in Baroque music.

Texture. Classical music was usually in homophonic texture, often a single melodic line with accompaniment. The most typical accompaniment pattern was the *Alberti bass*, named for the Pre-Classical composer Domenico Alberti (1710-1740). Polyphonic texture did not disappear completely, however fugues and other polyphonic forms were rarely written. Another aspect of Classical texture was the prevalence of thin, light sonorities as opposed to the predominantly massive sounds of Baroque music.

Melodic Style. Classical melodies were more concise with more thematic unity than the long, continuous lines of Baroque music. Classical melodies were generally diatonic.

Harmony. Classical harmony was overall less complex than Baroque harmony. More emphasis was given to primary triads, and diatonic harmony was more typical than chromatic. Chords were usually triadic, and seventh chords were used sparingly.

Improvisation. The art of improvisation died out with the disappearance of the basso continuo. All harmony was written out. Composers became more specific and consistent with the indications of ornamentation, phrasing, dynamics, and other details formerly left to the discretion of the performer.

Absolute Music. The classical period favored what is called *absolute music*: music which does not attempt to describe extra-musical things nor include descriptive titles.

Classical Composers.

Beethoven, Ludwig van (Germany, 1770-1827)

Clementi, Muzio (b. Italy 1752 - d. England 1832)

Czerny, Carl (Austria, 1791-1857)

Haydn, Joseph (Austria, 1732-1809)

Kuhlau, Friedrich (b. Germany 1786 - d. Denmark 1832)

Mozart, Wolfgang Amadeus (Austria, 1756-1791)

Pleyel, Ignaz (France, 1757-1831)

Türk, Daniel Gottlob (Germany, 1756-1832)

Classical Period Pianos. The possibilities of combining the sustaining tone of the clavichord with the power of the harpsichord were no doubt alluring to musicians and keyboard builders of the 17th century. It is not surprising that three inventors working independently in different countries perceived the hammer action piano concept at about the same time: Cristofori in Italy (1709), Marius in France (1716), and Schroter in Germany (1717). Credit is given to Bartolomeo Cristofori, curator of musical instruments for the wealthy Medici family in Florence, for producing the first piano. Cristofori called his invention a *gravicembalo col piano e forte* (a keyboard instrument which can play soft and loud). The ability of the early piano to produce graded dynamics (crescendos and diminuendos), plus its sustaining quality appealed to composers and keyboard makers of the time. By about 1728, Cristofori had improved his pianoforte by constructing a much stronger case than had been used for harpsichords to withstand the increased strain of heavier strings. The action at this time resembled the basic mechanics of the modern piano: escapement device, a back check regulating the fall of the hammer, and a damper for each key. Pianoforte building was continued by craftsmen such as Gottfried Silbermann, and his pupils Johannes Zumpe and Americus Becker who went to London to establish English pianoforte building. One of Silbermann's most talented pupils, Johann Stein, carried Viennese pianoforte making to new heights, and his instruments were preferred by Mozart, Beethoven, and others. The early pianos were small and produced a light, delicate sound. Mozart's piano had a range of not quite five octaves. A piano built by Broadwood in 1817 for Beethoven had a range of six octaves. It is interesting to note that J. S. Bach played one of Silbermann's pianos, and although he praised its tone, he complained that it was too weak in the treble, and it was too hard to play (stiff action).

3. The Romantic Period (1825-1900)

The period of time from about 1825 to 1900 is known as the Romantic period. However, aspects of romanticism appeared before 1825 and continued well into the 20th century.

Historical Context. Progress in science and engineering (photography, the railway and steamboat, steel production, electricity, the telephone and telegraph, and other innovations) influenced the cultural, economic, political, and social orders of the 19th century. The growth of technology expanded the Industrial Revolution in Europe and created new social and economic dilemmas: the development of capitalism and the appearance of socialism. 19th century conflicts included the Crimean War (1854-1856), the Civil War in the United States (1861-1865), and the Franco-Prussian War (1870-1871). The most important movement in art was French Impressionism in the second half of the century, represented by Manet, Degas, Monet and Renoir. Related to this movement were the French symbolist poets Verlaine, Mallarmé, and Rimbaud. Prominent philosophers of the period included Hegel and Nietzsche. It was the era of great Romantic literature: Byron, Wordsworth, Dickens, Keats, Schiller, Goethe, Heine, E. T. A. Hoffmann, Lamartine, Hugo, Flaubert, Emerson, Poe, Mark Twain, and many others.

Romantic Music. Romanticism, perceived as the antonym of classicism, implies the Dionysian ideals of ancient Greece: pathos, subjectivity, emotionalism, placing instinct over reason and sentiment over precise form. The 19th century was a time characterized by the desire for individualism and nationalism. Composers of the Romantic period became more socially and economically independent, no longer relying on the patronage of the church or aristocracy. Music was generally composed for one of two settings: the concert hall or the more intimate salon. There were notable extremes in length of compositions: extensive works (concertos, symphonies, operas) and shorter works (songs and piano pieces). Composers developed a greater affinity with poetry, literature, and art, and as a result favored more descriptive or "programmatic" music. The virtuoso concert performer became a much admired musician, and virtuosity in music developed into a common trait. The Romantic period is a particularly rich era for pianists because it significantly expanded the amount of repertoire for the piano. Nationalism also became a notable trend. Composers deliberately incorporated national styles by using folklore as subjects for operas, songs, and programmatic music, often using folk tunes and folk styles in their compositions.

Melody. Melodies in Romantic music generally have qualities of personal warmth and expressiveness, a more lyrical style, and more flexible phrase structure.

Harmony. The harmonic language of the Romantic period became an important means for expression through expanded chord structure and progressions. Chromaticism and modulation played important roles, along with a freer treatment of dissonance and the frequent appearance of seventh chords.

Tonality. Music of the Romantic period was still tonal (in a central key). However, the feeling of being in a key was frequently obscured by extended chromatic modulations to unrelated keys. This trend paved the way for radically new concepts of tonality in the 20th century.

Texture. Music of the Romantic period was primarily in homophonic texture yet included frequent use of secondary melodies and/or polyphonic techniques. The sonority of Romantic music was notable for a marked increase in the richness of sound.

Dynamics. Composers of the Romantic period exploited the inherent possibilities of dynamics for emotional expression. It became characteristic of the period to use a wide range of dynamic levels between loud and soft and extensive use of crescendo and diminuendo.

Form. Content and subjective expression became more important than strict musical form. As a result, forms such as binary, ternary, sonata-allegro, rondo, etc., were generally freer, more variable, and often less distinct than in the Classical period. Short piano pieces were often given descriptive titles and are called *character pieces*. They include pieces with such titles as *arabesque, ballad, intermezzo, nocturne, rhapsody, impromptu, bagatelle, songs without words*, and descriptive titles such as *Venetian Boat Song, Butterfly, March of the Dwarfs*, etc. Stylized dances such as the *waltz, mazurka*, and *polonaise* became a significant portion of the piano repertoire. The *etude*, basically a study featuring some technical aspect of performance (scales, arpeggios, octave, chords, etc.) was composed as a virtuoso piece for concert audiences.

Romantic Composers.

Brahms, Johannes (Germany, 1833-1897)
Burgmüller, Friedrich (b. Germany 1806-d. France 1874)
Heller, Stephan (Germany, 1814-1888)
Chopin, Frédéric (b. Poland 1810- d. France 1849)
Grieg, Edvard (Norway, 1843-1907)
Liszt, Franz (Hungary, 1811-1886)

Mendelssohn, Felix (Germany, 1809-1847)
Schubert, Franz (Austria, 1797-1828)
Schumann, Robert (Germany, 1810-1856)
Spindler, Fritz (Germany, 1817-1905)
Streabbog, Jean Louis (France, 1835-1886)
Tchaikovsky, Peter Ilyich (Russia, 1840-1893)

Romantic Period Pianos. The period of 1760 to 1830 was one of great activity in the development of the piano. The French piano builders Sebastien and Erard developed an instrument with greater tone using a larger sound board (1776-1777). Because of the piano's capacity for sonority, dynamic range, and gradations between loud and soft, it became the Romantic instrument of choice. It provided composers and performers with possibilities of emotional expression ranging from intimate to grandiose, from delicate lyricism to bombastic showiness. The damper pedal enabled composers to experiment with new harmonic effects, and the improved keyboard mechanism stimulated new idioms, technics, and virtuosity.

4. The 20th Century (1900-2000)

The 20th century is an era in which the rapidity and significance of changes are unparalleled in history. Events and developments in political, social, scientific, and cultural history profoundly influenced the course of music.

Historical Context. Two global wars in the first half of the 20th century had powerful impacts on world history: World War I (1914-1918) and World War II (1939-1945). Each conflict was followed by an effort to establish world government: the League of Nations (1920-46) and the United Nations (established in 1946). The Bolshevik Revolution in 1917 marked the emergence of Communism and of Russia as a world power. Conflicts since the mid-century were the Korean War (1950-1953), the Arab-Israeli conflict, and the Vietnam wars. A political and ideological struggle between the Soviet Union and the United States after World War II was known as the Cold War, a period of nonmilitary activity, but one marked by a major armaments race.

Tremendous advances in science and engineering and their application to industry affected social, economic, and cultural history. Extensive progress took place in biology, chemistry, physics, and astronomy. Remarkable developments in technology were made in the areas of communication, transportation, and medicine. Some specific innovations include radio, television, atomic energy, jet propulsion, computers, antibiotics, exploration of space and of suboceanic areas, and, especially relevant to music, high-fidelity sound transmission.

As with all periods in history, the spirit of the times is reflected in the arts. 20th century trends include frequent and rapid changes, and experimentation with new forms. A general trend away from realism and toward abstract and subjective expression is particularly apparent in the visual arts. Important trends in art include expressionism, cubism, surrealism, pop art, minimal art, and conceptual art. Styles in literature, poetry, and theater also reflect the era: social protest, existentialism, pessimism and despair, absurdity, and intentional "shock value" are distinct traits.

20th Century Music. From a historical point of view, the study of 20th century music poses a number of problems not encountered in previous periods. So far, no satisfactory name has been devised (comparable with Baroque, Classical, or Romantic) for 20th century music. The expression "contemporary period" is frequently used, yet is rather misleading since it implies that which is current, as opposed to that which was heard in previous decades of the 20th century. The expression "modern music" is also frequently used, but its implications are so variable that it is almost meaningless. Due to the enormous quantity of music written since 1900, the extraordinary diversity of trends, styles and technics, and the rapidity and frequency of change, it is difficult to perceive and evaluate 20th century music as a coordinated whole. Unlike previous periods, no single style represents the 20th century, or even a appreciable portion of it. The elements of melody, harmony, tonality, texture, rhythm, and form are so complex and varied in 20th century music that they virtually preclude the systematic analysis that can be applied to the music of previous periods.

Several important styles emerged among the diversity of music in the 20th century. Some styles are more prominent than others, and some of longer duration than others. The various styles of 20th century music frequently overlap in their development and are not necessarily in chronological order. Also, they are often not distinctly separate developments. The unique character of one composer may be a composite of more than one style. Several of the important styles are Late Romanticism, Impressionism, Neo-Classicism, and Jazz.

Late Romantic Music. While revolutionary new styles were appearing in the early decades of the 20th century, trends of the Romantic period prevailed. Subjectivity, emotionalism, and programmatic music were traits that remained even in compositions which used new harmonies, rhythms, and tonalities.

Late Romantic Composers

Ernst von Dohnanyi (Hungary, 1877-1960)	Edward MacDowell (USA, 1860-1908)
Anatol Liadov (Russia, 1855-1914)	Sergei Rachmaninoff (Russia, 1873-1943)

Impressionist Music. Impressionism, often referred to as a "transitional period", was the first important trend leading to the changing styles of the 20th century. It paralleled the French movements in painting and poetry, and was largely a reaction against the Romantic period. Although Impressionism shares some common traits with Romantic music (it is generally subjective and programmatic), it abandoned traditional compositional technics in several ways. It may be described as having a high degree of delicacy, vagueness of form, and generally a "luminous fog" atmosphere. Specific technics include the use of open chords (5ths and octaves without 3rds), parallel chords and other unconventional chord progressions, whole tone scales, and freer treatment of meter.

Impressionist Composers.

Claude Debussy (France, 1862-1918)	Maurice Ravel (France, 1875-1937)
Francis Poulenc (France, 1899-1963)	Eric Satie (France, 1866-1925)

Neo-Classical Music. Neo-classicism is one of the most prominent and prevailing styles in music of the 20th century. It appeared about 1920, and continues through the entire century. Neo-classical music uses pre-romantic period ideals of objectivity, and clarity of form. It also revives polyphonic textures and forms of the Baroque period (fugue, toccata, etc.) while using 20th century concepts of harmony, melody, tonality, and rhythm.

Neo-Classical Composers

Paul Hindemith (Germany, 1895-1963)	Gian Carlo Menotti (Italy, 1911-)
Norman Dello Joio (USA, 1913-)	Sergei Prokofiev (Russia, 1891-1953)
Dmitri Kabalevsky (Russia, 1904-1987)	Igor Stravinsky (Russia, 1882-1971)
Aram Khachaturian (Russia, 1903-1978)	Alexander Tcherepnin (Russia, 1899-1977)

Jazz. Particularly a 20th century phenomenon, and primarily an American innovation in popular music, Jazz is an important style which has influenced many trends of serious composition. In its broadest definition, Jazz is improvised instrumental dance music. However, the variety of Jazz styles preclude summation in one concise category. The various types of Jazz include *Ragtime, Blues, Dixieland, Big Band, Swing, Boogie-Woogie, Bop, Progressive Jazz, Cool Jazz, Third-Stream,* and *Rock and Roll.* As well as influencing the myriad of trends of popular music of the 20th century, many "classical" composers have incorporated Jazz elements into their music.

20th Century Compositional Techniques. In addition to the various new styles of music discussed above, there are significant changes in compositional techniques in music of the 20th century. These changes are evident primarily in the elements of rhythm, melody, harmony, and tonality. However, it should be understood that not all music of the 20th century is a reflection of radical change in all respects. Any 20th century composition may have one or two elements that reflect 20th century technics, and not necessarily to the extreme. The music of the 20th century ranges from ultra-conservative to avant-garde, most of which lies somewhere between the two extremes.

Meter and Rhythm. Composers of the 20th century sought new metric and rhythmic effects. In general, rhythm is used with more complexity, variety, and flexibility. Odd-numbered time signatures such as $\frac{5}{2}$ and $\frac{7}{4}$ are commonly found. Asymmetrical groupings of beats are used to create rhythmic effects. For example, in $\frac{7}{8}$, beats may be felt in patterns such as 3-2-2 or 2-2-3. Occasionaly, the time signature may be written as $\mathbf{2+\frac{2}{8}+3}$. In a more dramatic attempt at rhythmic flexibility, some composers omitted bar lines altogether.

Melody. Although many melodies in 20th century music are conservative, certain melodic characteristics are distinctly 20th century innovations. More extreme melodic styles include *disjunct melodies* (wide leaps from one note to the next), *angularity* (alternating upward and downward direction), and the use of dissonant intervals. Unconventional scales such as the *whole tone scale, pentatonic scale*, and *modal scales* also contribute to 20th century melodic styles.

Harmony. No element of 20th century music manifests more radical change than harmony. The tertian construction of chords (chords built with intervals of 3rds), such as triads and seventh chords, was augmented with the addition of more 3rds, resulting in 9th, 11th, and 13th chords. New types of 20th century chord construction include *quartal harmony* (chords built in 4ths), *tone clusters* and *polychords* (two or more different chords used simultaneously). Traditional chord progressions are largely abandoned in 20th century music and often replaced with arbitrary progressions, frequently involving chords with roots not related to the key. 20th century harmonic effects are often created with simple triads moving in parallel motion. One of the most distinct characteristics of 20th century harmony is the extent and degree to which dissonance is used. Unlike conventional harmony of the Baroque, Classical and Romantic periods, resolution of dissonance is not a prerequisite.

Tonality. Towards the end of the Romantic period, tonality (the feeling of being in a key, or gravitating towards a tonic note) was often obscured with increased chromaticism and prolonged modulations. Music of the 20th century departs further from traditional tonal concepts. 20th century innovations include *bitonality* (the use of two keys at the same time) and *polytonality* (the use of three or more keys at the same time) and *atonality* (the absence of any tonal center or key feeling). New scale constructions and the prolonged used of dissonance also contribute to tonal ambiguity.

Serialism. Serial music is constructed on the basis of a recurrent series of notes, rhythms, dynamics or other elements. Serialism first appeared in the 1920's with the development of the *twelve-tone row*. Serialism is related to both atonality and new concepts of form and structure in music.

20th Century Composers. Although names of composers were included in the preceding discussions of the various 20th century musical styles, many 20th century composers use a variety of styles and techniques and defy exact categorization. Listed here are a number of significant composers not named in the aforementioned text.

Agay, Denes (USA, 1911-)	Ginastera, Alberto (Argentina, 1916-1983)
Barber, Samuel (USA, 1910-1981)	Muczynski, Robert (USA, 1929 -)
Bartók, Béla (b. Hungary 1881 d. New York 1945)	Pinto, Octavio (Brazil, 1890-1950)
Bastien, James (USA, 1934-)	Rocherolle, Eugénie (USA, 1936-)
Britten, Benjamin (England, 1913-1976)	Shostakovich, Dmitri (Russia, 1906-1975)
Copland, Aaron (America, 1900-1990)	Tansman, Alexander (B. Poland 1897, d. France 1986)
Gershwin, George (USA 1898-1937)	Turina, Joaquin (Spain, 1882-1949)
Gillock, Willian (USA, 1917-1996)	Villa-Lobos, Heitor (Brazil, 1887-1959)

Unit 19
Signs and Terms

Dynamics

TERM	SIGN	MEANING
pianississimo	*ppp*	very, very soft
pianissimo	*pp*	very soft
piano	*p*	soft
mezzo piano	*mp*	medium soft
mezzo forte	*mf*	medium loud
forte	*f*	loud
fortissimo	*ff*	very loud
fortississimo	*fff*	very, very loud
crescendo (cresc.)	<	gradually louder
diminuendo (dim.)	>	gradually softer
fortepiano	*fp*	loud, then immediately soft
sotto voce		in an undertone, subdued

Tempo

TERM	MEANING
adagio	slow
allegro	fast (also means cheerful, happy)
allegretto	somewhat fast (slower than allegro)
andante	walking tempo (flowing)
andantino	slightly faster than andante
animato	animated, with spirit
con moto	with motion
largo	stately, broad, a very slow tempo
lento	slow
moderato	moderately
presto	very fast
vivace	lively, quick
vivo	lively

Changing Tempo

accelerando (accel.)	gradually faster
a tempo	return to the original tempo
allargando	broadening, gradually slower
meno mosso	less motion, slower
piu mosso	more motion, faster
rallentando (rall., rallent.)	gradually slower
ritardando (rit.)	gradually slower
ritenuto	held back, suddenly slower
rubato	freely, flexible; slight accelerandos and ritardandos used for musical expression

Character or Style

TERM	MEANING
cantabile	in a singing manner
con brio	with spirit
con fuoco	with fire
dolce	gently, sweetly
doloroso	sadly, sorrowfully
espressivo	expressively
---etto	little
giocoso	humorous
grazioso	gracefully
--ino	little
leggiero	lightly
meno	less
molto	much, very
pesante	heavily, ponderously
piu	more
poco	little
robusto	boldly, robustly
scherzando	playful
sempre	always
senza	without
simile	in a similar manner, same
smorzando	fading away
spiritoso	spirited
subito	suddenly
tranquillo	peacefully, tranquil, calm

Articulation

TERM	SIGN	MEANING
accent	>	strong emphasis
legato	⌒	smooth, connected
sforzando	*sf* or *sfz*	sudden strong accent
sostenuto		sustained, legato
staccato	●	short, detached
tenuto		hold full value; slight emphasis

Additional Signs and Terms

Alberti bass: An accompaniment pattern using a three note chord.  The notes of the chord are played bottom - top - middle - top.

Arpeggio: The notes of a chord played one after another instead of together.  The notes of an arpeggio may be written out, or indicated by a wavy line to the left of the chord.

Chromatic Half Step: A half step with two notes of the same letter name (for example: C to C♯).

Diatonic Half Step: A half step with notes of different letter names (for example: C to D♭).

D. C. al Fine (da capo al fine): Play from the beginning to the *fine* (end).

Fermata ⌢ : Hold a note longer than its time value.

Grace Note ♪ : A grace note is printed in small type. It is not counted in the rhythm; it is played quickly, almost together with the next note.

m.d. (mano destra): Right hand.

m.s. (mano sinistra): Left hand.

Octave Sign *8va_____*

When the octave sign is placed over notes, play one octave (eight notes) higher than written. When the octave sign is placed under notes, play one octave lower than written.

Opus (Op.): Work. The term is usually used with a number to indicate the chronological order of music written by a composer (Op. 1, Op. 2, Op. 3, etc.).

Pedal Point: A consistent note that is held, repeated, or returned to regularly as harmonies change.

Pedal Sign ⌞_____⌟ : The pedal sign shows when to press and lift the damper (right) pedal.

tre corde: Release the soft (left) pedal.

una corda: Depress the soft (left) pedal.

Ornaments

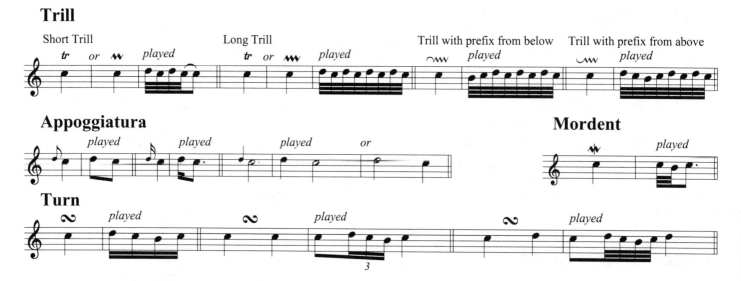

Melodic Phrase Structure

Augmentation: The presentation of a melody or motive with the note values doubled.

Canon: A style of writing in which an extended melody is imitated strictly and entirely in one or more voices.

Diminution: The presentation of a melody or motive with the note values halved.

Imitation: The immediate restatement of a melody or motive in another voice or hand.

Motive (motif): A motive is a short melodic or rhythmic pattern that appears throughout a piece. When the motive appears in the music, it may begin on a different note, the rhythm may change slightly, or the motive may be inverted.

Repetition: Repetition occurs when a melodic or rhythmic pattern is repeated.

Sequence: A sequence occurs when a melodic pattern in repeated at a higher or lower pitch, usually a 2nd or 3rd above or below the original pattern.

Musical Forms

Binary Form: Music in binary form has two sections: section **A** and section **B**. Each section is usually repeated. The **A** section often ends on the dominant note, and the **B** section ends on the tonic.

Ternary form: Music written in ternary form has three sections: section **A,** section **B,** and a repeat of section **A.** The two sections are often contrasting in character or style.

Sonata: The sonata is a composition for piano which has separate sections called movements. The movements are usually contrasting in tempo and character.

Sonatina: The sonatina is a short sonata, usually designed for instruction. A sonatina may have one, two, or three movements. The movements are usually contrasting in tempo and character.

Sonata-Allegro Form: First movements of sonatas and sonatinas are frequently written in a form called "sonata-allegro" or *first movement* form:

    1. **Exposition** section
        A. first theme: tonic key
        B. second theme: dominant key, or relative Major if the piece is in minor key.
        C. closing theme (optional)

    2. **Development** section
        Themes are presented in new keys. New themes may be added.

    3. **Recapitulation** section
        A. first theme: tonic key
        B. second theme: tonic key
        C. closing theme (optional)

Rondo: Music in rondo form has a recurring theme (A) that appears between contrasting sec-tions (B, C, etc.).

Texture in Music

Polyphonic Texture: Music with two or more independent parts or voices (melodies).

Homophonic Texture: Music with melody and accompaniment.

74

1. Write the meaning of each dynamic term.

sotto voce _____   mezzo forte _____

forte piano _____   diminuendo _____

2. Write the meaning of each tempo term.

con moto _____   vivace _____

animato _____   adagio _____

lento _____   presto _____

andante _____   piu mosso _____

accelerando _____   ritenuto _____

rubato _____

3. Write the meaning of each character or style term.

smorzando _____   con fuoco _____

leggiero _____   tranquillo _____

molto _____   cantabile _____

senza _____   meno _____

dolce _____   subito _____

doloroso _____   simile _____

piu _____   poco _____

pesante _____   espressivo _____

4. Write the meaning of each articulation term.

staccato _____   legato _____

sostenuto _____   tenuto _____

accent _____   sforzando _____

5. Define the following terms.

Pedal Point _____

Diatonic Half Step _____

Chromatic Half Step _____

Opus _____

Motive _____

Augmentation _____

Diminution _____

Binary form _____

Ternary form _____

Polyphonic _____

Homophonic _____

m. d. _____ m. s. _____

tre corda _____ una corda _____

6. Write the name of each ornament

tr or 𝄽 _____ ♪♩ _____

∾ _____ 𝄿 _____

7. Match each ornament with its correct performance.

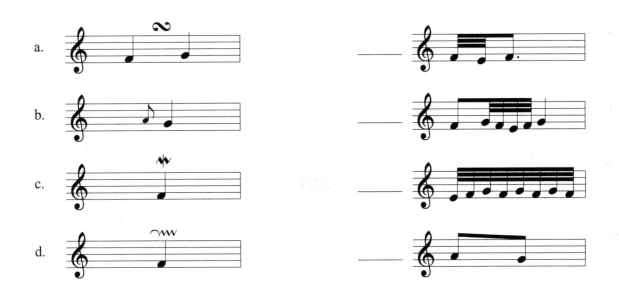

Unit 20
Ear Training

Practice #1

Listen as your teacher plays one interval from each pair. Circle the one you hear.

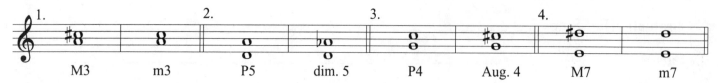

Listen as your teacher plays one seventh chord from each pair. Circle the one you hear.

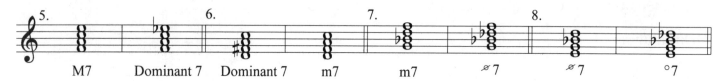

Listen as your teacher plays a root position or first inversion seventh chord. Circle the one you hear.

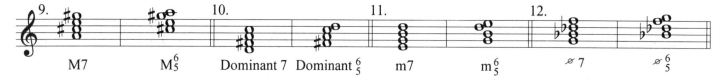

13. Listen as your teacher plays one of the scales below. Check (✓) the one you hear.

Listen as your teacher plays one chord progression from each pair. Check (✓) the one you hear.

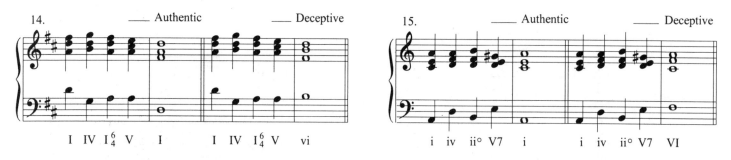

16. Listen as your teacher plays one of the phrases below. Check (✓) the one you hear.

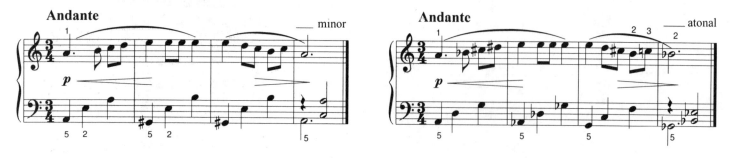

Practice #2

Listen as your teacher plays one interval from each pair. Circle the one you hear.

Listen as your teacher plays one seventh chord from each pair. Circle the one you hear.

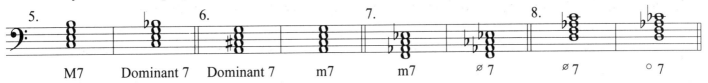

Listen as your teacher plays a root position or first inversion seventh chord. Circle the one you hear.

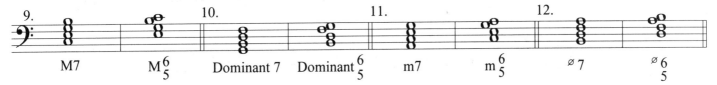

13. Listen as your teacher plays one of the scales below. Check (✓) the one you hear.

Listen as your teacher plays one chord progression from each pair. Check (✓) the one your hear.

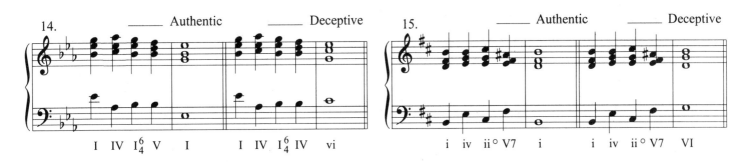

16. Listen as your teacher plays one of the phrases below. Check (✓) the one you hear.

Unit 21
Sight Reading

The best way to become a good sight reader is to read new music every day.

1. Before you sight read, look through the entire piece and observe:
    - the key signature
    - the time signature
    - the clef signs
    - dynamics
    - accidentals
    - slurs, ties, staccatos, accents, etc.
    - rhythmic and melodic patterns

2. Find the first note and finger number for each hand.

3. Play slowly.
    - Use a metronome to keep a steady beat.
    - Count one measure aloud before you begin to play.
    - Continue to count aloud as you play.

4. Keep your eyes on the music.
    - Avoid looking up and down from the music to your hands.
    - Look ahead to see what is next.

5. Keep going, even if you make some mistakes; avoid going back to "fix" anything.

6. After you sight read, evaluate your playing.
    - Were the notes and rhythm correct?
    - Were the dynamics and articulation markings clear and distinct?
    - Did the music continue to move forward as you maintained a steady beat?

7. Sight read the music again.
    - Concentrate on correcting any previous mistakes.
    - Set a goal for a perfect performance by the third reading.

Review Test

1. Write each key signature.

    Ab Major   B Major   Gb Major   C# minor   Bb minor   D# minor

2. Add the correct accidentals to form each scale.

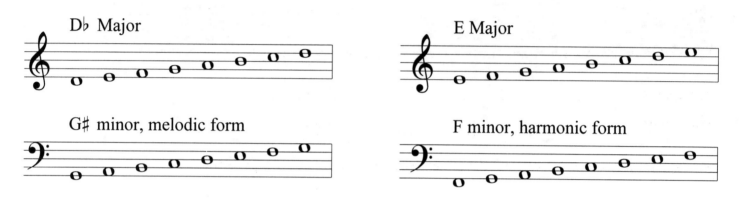

Db Major   E Major

G# minor, melodic form   F minor, harmonic form

3. Name each interval (observe the key signature).

4. Draw one note above the given one to form each interval (observe the key signature).

    m6   d4   A6   M7   M3   M2

5. Draw the following seventh chords.

    DM7   Em$\frac{6}{5}$ B$^{\varnothing}\frac{4}{3}$ A$^{\circ}\frac{4}{2}$

6. Draw the dominant seventh chord for each key according to the figured bass.

D Major   G minor   A Major   C minor

    V7   V$\frac{6}{5}$ V$\frac{4}{3}$ V$\frac{4}{2}$

7. Write the meaning of each tempo term.

andantino _____   largo _____

allargando _____   meno mosso _____

8. Write the meaning of each character or style term.

con brio _____   giocoso _____

grazioso _____   scherzando _____

sempre _____   spiritoso _____

9. Write one characteristic of each of these dances of a Baroque suite.

Allemande _____   Courante _____

Sarabande _____   Gigue _____

10. Write the names of four optional dance movements of a Baroque suite.

_____   _____   _____   _____

11. Name the three main sections of a piece in Sonata-Allegro form. Describe each section.

1. _____

_____

_____

2. _____

_____

_____

3. _____

_____

_____

12. Write the names of two composers from each of the following periods of music history.

Baroque	Classical	Romantic	Impressionist/ Late Romantic	20th Century
_____	_____	_____	_____	_____
_____	_____	_____	_____	_____

Sonata, Op. 2, No. 1

First Movement, measures 101-151

Ludwig van Beethoven
(1770-1827)

The music on page 82 is from a sonata by Beethoven. Answer the following questions about the music.

13. The time signature for this piece is $\frac{2}{2}$. Write the sign typically used for this time signature. _____

14. What is the term for the time signature of this piece? _____

15. What is the meter of this piece? _____

16. In what minor key is this piece? _____

17. What type of non-chord tone is the F in measure 108? _____

18. Write the Roman numerals and figured bass for the underlined chords in measures 101-108 on the lines under the staff according to the key you named in question 16.

19. Name the cadence in measures 107-108. _____

20. Name the harmonic intervals in the left hand in measures 111-114. _____

_____

_____

_____

21. Name the note that is a pedal point in measures 119-124. _____

22. What type of non-chord tone is the D♭ in measure 119? _____

23. What is the term for the left hand accompaniment pattern in measures 125-130? _____

24. Circle the A6 chord in measure 127. Is this A6 chord Italian, French or German? _____

25. What compositional device is used in measures 129-130.

Repetition

Sequence

26. Circle the term that describes the rhythm of the left hand in measures 131-133.

Hemiola

Syncopation

27. What compositonal device is used in measures 139-143?

Repetition

Sequence

28. Write the Roman numeral and figured bass for the secondary dominant in measure 145. ___ of ___

29. Write the Roman numeral and figured bass for the secondary dominant in measure 147. ___ of ___

30. Name the cadence in measures 150-151. _____

Fugue No. 26

WTC Book One

Johann Sebastian Bach
(1685-1750)

The music on page 84 is a fugue by Bach. Answer questions 31-37 about the music.

31. In what key is this piece?   _____

32. How many voices are in this fugue?   _____

33. Is the answer real or tonal?   _____

34. In what measure does the first exposition end?   _____

35. In what key does the music cadence at the end of the first exposition?   _____

36. What compositional device is used in measures 24-27?   Imitation

                                                                        Sequence

37. What is the term for the structure of measures 28-29?   Stretto

                                                                        Inversion

38. Match the following terms and definitions.

   a. Theme and Variations   _____   A musical from that has a recurring section (A) that alternates with contrasting sections (B, C, etc.)

   b. Quartal Harmony   _____   The use of two or more keys at the same time

   c. Rondo   _____   Music in which elements such as pitch, rhythm, dynamics, articulations, etc. are used to organize the structure of a composition

   d. Polytonality   _____   A musical form in which a theme is followed by any number of modified restatements

   e. Extended Tertian Harmony   _____   Ascending intervals changed into the corresponding descending intervals and vice versa

   f. Atonality   _____   A section of a fugue that does not include a statement of the subject

   g. Serialism   _____   Chords built in fourths

   h. Inversion   _____   The avoidance of any key or tonal center

   i. Episode   _____   The use of additional thirds above the 7th, resulting in 9th, 11th and 13th chords